SOCIAL AND ECONOMIC FACTORS AFFECTING MORTALITY

BY

B. BENJAMIN

Director of Statistics
Ministry of Health
London

MOUTON & CO
THE HAGUE · PARIS
1965

Contents / Table des matières

INTRODUCTION A LA COLLECTION VIII
INTRODUCTION TO THE SERIES IX
Introduction 1
Definition of social and economic factors 5
The measurement of social and economic factors 7
The problem of interdependence 9
Factor analysis 13
Urban typology 14
The level of living 17
Time changes in death rates 18
Generation mortality studies 19
Nutrition 21
Occupation 25
Age standardisation 27
Difficulties of interpretation 29
Limitations of occupational mortality investigations 33
Occupational differences 33
Urbanisation 35
Housing 37
Classification of housing conditions 38
Marriage 42
Climate and geography 44
Factors influencing peri-natal mortality 46
Education and culture 49
Availability of medical services 52
The mode of living 53
Socio-economic groups 58
Prospective studies 64
RÉSUMÉ FRANÇAIS 67
BIBLIOGRAPHY 75
AUTHOR INDEX 86

Introduction à la collection

Le Comité International pour la Documentation des Sciences Sociales a été créé en 1950 avec l'aide de l'Unesco. C'est une organisation internationale non gouvernementale, composée d'une vingtaine de spécialistes des diverses sciences sociales et de techniciens en matière bibliographique. Ses membres travaillent en liaison étroite avec le Conseil International des Sciences Sociales et avec les associations internationales spécialisées en ce domaine.

Une des principales tâches assumées par le Comité est l'établissement de bibliographies internationales. Quatre bibliographies, concernant respectivement la Sociologie, la Science économique, la Science politique et l'Anthropologie sociale et culturelle, sont rédigées chaque année et, après avoir été publiées depuis 1951 par l'Unesco, le sont depuis 1962 par Tavistock Publications, de Londres. D'autres travaux, tels que la préparation de catalogues, recueils d'analyses, répertoires, index... sont effectués régulièrement par le Comité dans le but de doter les sciences sociales d'un équipement documentaire.

La collection *Confluence* a pour objet de faire connaître l'état actuel des recherches sur des sujets donnés. Ceux-ci sont choisis en raison de leur caractère interdisciplinaire, c'est à dire du fait qu'ils intéressent plusieurs sciences sociales ou justifient d'approches multiples. De cette façon, le Comité espère contribuer au rapprochement des diverses disciplines.

La rédaction de chaque volume est confiée à un spécialiste qui en établit le manuscrit sous sa propre responsabilité. Un sous-comité de lecture est, dans chaque cas, appelé à se prononcer sur le manuscrit avant qu'il ne soit imprimé. Par ailleurs le Comité International donne à chaque auteur les indications lui permettant de se conformer à un modèle normalisé pour la présentation du rapport et la rédaction des références bibliographiques. Mais le Comité n'entend pas substituer sa responsabilité à celle de l'auteur qui signe le texte.

Introduction to the Series

The International Committee for Social Sciences Documentation was formed in 1950, with the support of Unesco. It is an international non-governmental organization, gathering some twenty scholars of the various social sciences and specialists of bibliographical work. Its members work in close cooperation with the International Social Science Council and the various specialized international associations.

One of the main tasks undertaken by the Committee is the preparation of international bibliographies. Four bibliographies, for Sociology, Economics, Political Science and Social and Cultural Anthropology, are compiled yearly; they were published from 1951 to 1961 by Unesco, and are published now by Tavistock Publications, London. Other tasks such as the preparation of catalogues, collections of abstracts, repertories, indexes... are regularly performed by the Committee in order to provide the social sciences with documentary tools.

The series *Confluence* is intended to publish surveys of current research on special subjects. These are chosen because of their interdisciplinary character, i.e. because they are of interest to several social sciences or because they warrant a multiple approach. By these means, the Committee hopes to contribute to the strengthening of relations between the various disciplines.

Each volume is written by an individual scholar, under his own responsibility. An editorial sub-committee reports on each manuscript before it is printed. The International Committee provides to each author instructions as to the standard form of the report and the bibliographical references. But the Committee does not take over responsibility for the report from the author who signs it.

Social and Economic Factors affecting Mortality

INTRODUCTION

Death is the end result of a chain of events or conditions which may occupy a short space of time as in homicide or in sudden death in a road accident, or may be prolonged over a number of years, even decades, as in some degenerative condition such as progressive muscular atrophy or in some types of malignancy of slow growth. The internationally accepted system of certification, and therefore of classification, of cause of death calls for the assessment of an underlying cause of death, i.e. a condition which may be regarded as the first of the chain of events leading to death. What is identifiable as the primary condition may not be recognised until quite late in a period during which death may be an inevitable end result. There are many degrees of illhealth between wellbeing and the near moribund state and the descent may be slow and insidious toward a state where the affected person may feel unwell or some other observer may recognise signs and symptoms of disease (Benjamin, 1957, no. 1). Measurements of mortality and of influences of significance thereon must be conducted within the framework of available statistical analysis. Such measurements must therefore be in terms of not the whole continuum of events leading to death but of those, summarised in the death certificate, which can be recognised in medical practice. We are looking very often at only the top of the iceberg much of which lies submerged and beyond observation.

The human body is a complex organism in continual reaction with the environment in which it exists and it is a matter of some difficulty to isolate those features of the environment which may have a bearing either on the inception of the fatal chain of events or on the events themselves especially when, as we have seen, the events observed may only be those medically recognisable in a terminal phase. The illness leading to death may occur when the person is in a social environment quite different from that which perhaps in some subtle way has predisposed him to the observed illness. Factors affecting this predisposition may go back further still; they may not be environmental but genetic. It has been plausibly suggested that those deaths from lung cancer which appear to be associated with the smoking of cigarettes occur in genotypes predisposed both to smoking and to lung cancer. This hypothesis does not appear to be consistent with secular changes in mortality from lung cancer in Western society, but it serves to illustrate the wide range of factors with which we have to deal.

Quite apart from those factors which affect mortality and which are clearly seen to operate from outside the human body, for example injury, exposure, infection, there are others which covertly disturb bodily function or affect bodily wear and tear; they may operate only to alter the rate of growing old and the speed of degeneration.

All must die eventually. In the absence of exogenous forces of destruction it appears likely that the continual process of cellular renewal which takes place within the human body must ultimately break down and fail to the extent that life is no longer supportable.

The present status of research on ageing opens up exciting possibilities of discovery of the significant process of senescence and the natural potential for human survival. The main biological factors involved are deterioration of irreplaceable structures, the cumulative effect of past injuries that have not been completely or perfectly repaired, and progressive morphogenic changes in the nature and specificity of cellular responses and organ functions (Comfort, 1956, no. 18). Senescence is a property acquired as a potentiality through the operation of evolutionary forces directed toward other biological goals.

Longevity is determined to some extent by genetic factors. For example experiments have shown that different strains of fruit flies with widely different life spans could be isolated by selective breeding. Other similar experiments with the rotifer have shown that offspring from young mothers lives longer than those from old and that the increase in longevity is progressive over successive generations. Matings between long-lived mice have shown that parental influences contribute to determine longevity. Studies on old twins (Moore, J. E., Merritt, H. H., and Mosselink, R. J., 1956, no. 19) by Kallman indicate that the same is true of humans.

2

Ageing and death occur in all animals but the pattern varies with the species. Warm blooded mammals grow rapidly during early life, then experience a period of relatively stable size after attaining sexual maturity and finally undergo a decline that ends in death; they show evidence of declining physiological functions as maturity progresses (for example the number of eggs laid by birds diminishes with age). In contrast the cold blooded animals, which continue to grow throughout life and often live to advanced ages, do not experience a decline in physiological functions (the number of eggs laid by snakes increases with age). It has been suggested that these differences reflect different rates of living, the rate being slower for cold-blooded animals, the metabolism of which drops to a low level during cold weather. The warm-blooded animals maintain a uniform temperature in cold weather and higher metabolic rates. Shortening of life span can be achieved in small aquatic animals and in insects by elevating body temperature; it can also be achieved by overfeeding. Early restriction of calorie intake lowers the growth rate and extends the life span of rats and mice. Whether or not the 'rate of living' theory is applicable to human populations it is clear that nutrition has an important influence on longevity. The difficulty with human populations is that it is not possible to carry out long term experiments of restriction of diet as a single variable. History has provided many "experiments" of nutritional inadequacy but this has always been associated with other concomitants of poverty or economic underdevelopment especially lethal infections so that the subjects of the "experiment" have not survived to benefit from any slowing up in the rate of living. Nutritional excesses are obviously deleterious to health – overweight subjects have higher mortality – but this is a different matter.

Conventional microscopic methods have shown that ageing is accompanied by the accumulation of pigments in cellular tissue (Andrew, 1952, no. 17). It is thought that these pigments represent the collection of waste products. More detailed examinations with the electron microscope have revealed changes in certain cellular components. Similar changes are also produced by infection and diet so that their precise relationship to ageing is not yet explained, but clearly important developments may be expected in this field. Other age changes in tissue have been demonstrated. There is an increase in the connective tissue surrounding individual cells. In general, aged tissues tend to show increased amounts of connective tissue, fat and other extracellular substances, and, in some tissues e.g. in the nervous system, a reduction in the number of normally functioning cells. Quantitative data are at

3

present lacking. There is also, with ageing, a progressive loss of elasticity of connective tissue.

The rate of metabolism of a tissue is reflected in the rate of utilising oxygen. This rate is lower in old tissues than in young. It is not known whether this is due to a reduction in the number of cells (which does occur with increased age), or to a lowering of metabolic activity. The problem will doubtless soon yield to the experimental ingenuity of the biochemists.

More is known about age changes in physiological performance (Shock, 1957, no. 20). For example, the average blood flow through the kidney decreases linearly from age 30 onward though at any one age the measurements of a group of individuals are widely dispersed. The amount of blood pumped by the heart under resting conditions, the average speed of conduction of a nerve impulse in a peripheral nerve, the maximum amount of air that can be expired from the lungs, muscular strength, and the excretion of certain hormones produced by the sex glands and the adrenal glands all show gradual reduction with increasing age. Other characteristics which are well maintained with advancing age in resting conditions e.g. fasting blood sugar level, are slower to recover from disturbance in older than in younger subjects. Reserve capacities are diminished in older subjects. Sex gland function decreased with age but not thyroid gland function or adrenal gland function. In so far as some of the physiological changes in old age may be due to actual loss of functioning tissue the importance of nutrition is underlined.

General nutritional findings are as follows. Laboratory studies using the metabolic balance technique in which a detailed chemical analysis is made of everything entering and leaving the human body have shown that older people in normal health, when given adequate intakes of specific food elements, are able to absorb them and to build them into the tissues of their bodies. Although the nutritional requirements of older persons may be different from those of younger persons the intake of proteins, minerals and vitamins must be maintained for healthy existence. Some workers have even suggested that the intake needs to be increased. In addition there is the as yet indeterminate role of unsaturated fats (mainly from animal sources) in the development of arteriosclerosis and the more generally deleterious effect of excess body weight.

Many of these ageing processes merge imperceptibly into dysfunction and conditions of degeneration which are recognisable clinically as disease patterns. For the purpose of this review it seems unprofitable (even though what has already been said indicates that the temptation is very great) to attempt to distinguish between clinically identifiable disease and ageing. We shall therefore concern ourselves with empirical relationships between observed mortality and measurable social and economic factors recognising that the mechanisms involved may stretch back a long way perhaps even to genetic susceptibilities in a manner beyond our present perception.

This does mean, however that it becomes exceedingly difficult to make any transition from statistical association between mortality changes and changes in cultural or economic factors to any precise formulation of hypotheses about causation. While it may be a simplification to avoid any distinction between disease and ageing there is still the difficulty that this also avoids the distinction between factors which promote an acceleration in the natural rate of ageing and those which either by some psychosomatic mechanism or by direct damage to the physical organism of man increase mortality. The observable outcome may be the same in each case; a rise in the rate of mortality from a medically defined cause of death in a particular age group. It could be argued immediately that this does not matter since the factors would from the mortality statistics, be *seen* to be operating, and that this is the simple object of our study.

DEFINITION OF SOCIAL AND ECONOMIC FACTORS

We shall be concerned in this study with a broad spectrum of elements which determine man's interaction with external conditions; his resistance to the inimical forces of nature, his approach to the economic struggle to supply himself with living needs, his position in society, participation in group behaviour, and attitude to social mores. We regard this whole process of adaptation to external stresses as reflective of health and failure to adapt as illhealth; we focus upon this process as the superficial mechanism of mortality variation. There are numerous distinct elements in the environment which influence this process of adaptation. We think immediately of mode of employment and working conditions, of intelligence and educational attainment, of other elements in the level of living – nutrition, clothing, housing, access to medical care and other services which foster well-being, even entertainment and sport – most of which are purchaseable and therefore related to income. Then too there is the cultural background, religion, social customs, art forms and modes of emotional expression. We are concerned with the more subtle mental stresses as well as the patent physical hardships built in to the social and economic environment.

5

The impact of community values on the implementation of programmes of health improvement or disease prevention has been well illustrated in the case studies collected by Benjamin Paul (1955, no. 68). In health education there is always the obstacle presented by cultural features which reflect the fundamental moral code of social conduct. Even the comparatively simple process of improving the consumption of cow's milk may come against the antithetical association, heavily charged with emotion, of cattle with witchcraft. In the sphere of psychiatry the irrational fear and suspicion of the abnormal is often a barrier to the rehabilitation of the mentally ill within the community. Even the induction of such a simple habit of rural hygiene as boiling drinking water can be opposed by quite complicated behavioural patterns; that is, of symbolic associations of "hot" and "cold" and feelings that it is socially degrading to admit that the household water supply is in need of boiling. To talk about the place of faith in healing is to oversimplify an extremely complicated network in the cultural system of a community in which simple physical symptoms are attributed to moral weakness. "Health practices and health ideas penetrate deeply into the domains of politics, philosophy, etiquette, religion, cosmology and kinship", and within these too there are social differentials.

In some instances the connection between the isolated factor and economic conditions may seem to be rather remote but it is nevertheless real. For example atmospheric pollution though widespread over a geographical area has to be more endured by those whose economic circumstances are such as to prevent them from moving their domicile or their employment to more salubrious areas. In general those who dwell in atmospherically polluted industrial areas of the north of England are of lower socio-economic groups than in the south and have a higher incidence of respiratory disease. (General Register Office, 1954, no. 15). Similarly it very often is the case that the risk of accidental injury or other occupational hazard is greater for those employments into which the more necessitous members of the community have been forced. This was true of coal mining, for example, at any rate initially. In time, of course, tradition and settlement reinforce the economic compulsion and whole communities become dependent upon such industries. Traditional attachment to an occupation may persist even when economic conditions change. Stevedoring is a hazardous occupation but in Britain, even in an era of full employment when easier and better paid jobs are available, sons still traditionally follow their fathers into the docks. Social mobility is not an inevitable or rapid process.

6

If observation of the causation of death is necessarily superficial, in a literal sense, observation of the variation in social, economic and cultural environment is equally lacking in specificity. For, in describing the surroundings of man we are dealing with a whole complex of elements of which we are well aware but which are difficult to quantify over the large groups in which the related mortality variations are to be observed. In the individual person it is practicable to measure or record employment, nutrition, housing conditions, ventilation, exposure to elements, urbanisation, position in family, educational attainment, religion, attitudes to people and social aspirations, domestic situation, participation in household life, social and physical habits, sleep, access to medical services, attitude to hygiene, intelligence and adaptability. Some of these records will be descriptive and not susceptible to statistical or group measurement. For many of the others it is not possible to obtain specific measurements for defined groups of persons.

What is more important it is not possible in relation to social and economic factors to treat the population of human beings as if they were forms of plant life capable of being subjected to designed factorial experiments to test environmental influences. You cannot submit a specific group of persons to a defined set of economic circumstances, not even in the least benevolent of totalitarian regimes. Apart from the ethical problem, there are practical difficulties. Economic and social conditions emerge from the interaction of people of diverse characteristics living together in groups; the economic and social conditions both determine and are determined by the behaviour and movement of the individuals in the group. It would be extremely difficult at the one time to create a stable set of economic circumstances and to separate a particular segment of the social group to be subjected to these circumstances.

The next best thing is to discover in the population, segments which are existing naturally and which are homogeneous in relation to specific factors, so that they would, as it were, lay themselves out as a factorial design. For example if one wanted to investigate the independent effects of socioeconomic group (grading by occupation, industry, and position within employment such as employer, manager, etc.) and housing density (persons per room in dwelling), one could proceed to select areas a, b, c, d, ... according to the following illustrative plan.

Socio-economic group (per cent of active population in employer, managerial, professional groups)	Housing Density, category				
	1	2	3	4	5
0-4	a h 1	m z	e j	c u	
5-9	n w	b k	etc.		
10-14	etc.				

The populations of areas b and k form a group uniquely specified in relation to socio-economic group and housing density, and the mortality of these groups may then be compared.

It is not often possible to obtain either a sufficient diversity of areas or even to make such a prior selection of areas. More often the data are limited to a number of adjacent areas for which the necessary population and death statistics are furnished and it is necessary to make what one can of the diversity of indicators available. An important difficulty here is that the social index (whatever it may be) will be an average value which may conceal considerable heterogeneity within the area (since the areas have not been selected on the grounds of homogeneity). This can lead to artefacts. For example the presence of a small group of low social status and high mortality might have more effect on mortality than on the social index for the area, leading to a departure from the normal inverse relationship between social status and mortality. This may be at the root of such departures referred to by Stockwell (1961, no. 54).

Those statistical measures which are normally available, are indicators compounding the forces of a number of these elements but not specific to any one of them. For example, income is measurable but clearly this is commonly higher for professional workers than for manual employees; higher incomes mean better housing conditions and other material advantages; and it is those with greater intelligence and a better educational attainment who secure jobs with higher incomes. For this reason it is difficult to obtain any degree of specificity in indicators. Each indicator compounds

elements the separate contributions of which cannot be separated. For the
same reason it is difficult to find indicators which do not overlap in their
content.

THE PROBLEM OF INTERDEPENDENCE

As an illustration the following statement shows the first-order correlation
coefficients measuring the association between a number of indicators for
the 28 main administrative areas which make up the County of London (the
inner part of the London Conurbation). The figures are taken from a study
of tuberculosis and social conditions relating to the years 1931-33 (Benjamin,
1953, no. 2).

Table 1. Zero Order Correlation Coefficients

	b	c	d	f	g	h	m	p	o
z	+.725	+.688	+.679	−.512	+.072	−.256	+.601	−.564	−.296
b		+.719	+.836	−.591	+.183	+.070	+.626	−.464	−.135
c			+.903	−.636	+.261	−.193	+.915	−.403	−.463
d				−.583	+.349	−.007	+.816	−.469	−.352
f					−.209	+.313	−.470	+.402	+.333
g						+.075	+.210	+.114	−.174
h							−.201	+.133	+.174
m								−.333	−.378
p									+.345

The position of the coefficient by row and column indicates the two indices
between which association is measured.

Index

z Death rate from pulmonary tuberculosis per 1,000 of population. Mean
   annual rate for 1931-33, computed from data provided by the Registrar
   General for England and Wales.

a Primary notification rate of new cases of pulmonary tuberculosis per
   1,000 living. Mean annual rate for 1931-33. Computed from returns
   made to the London County Council by the Borough Medical Officers of
   Health under the Public Health (Tuberculosis) Regulations, 1930.

b Social Index. Percentage of males aged 14 and over whose occupations
   were assigned to social classes IV and V at the 1931 Census. Computed
   according to the procedure given in the Registrar General's Statistical
   Review for 1934, Text, pp. 150 et seq.

9

c Percentage of population in private families living at a density of more than one and a half persons per room at 1931 Census. Extracted from Housing Report and Tables (Table 13).

d Percentage of males aged 14 and over unemployed at 1931 Census. Extracted from Occupation Tables (Table 16).

f Mean weights of school children expressed as a percentage of the London average, 1938. Computed from London County Council Report on Average Heights and Weights of School Children (No. 3464), Appendix I, pp. 10 et seq.

g Attendances at Tuberculosis dispensaries per case on the registers, 1932. Extracted from Annual Report of the London County Council, 1932, Vol. III, Part I, p. 36.

h Gross expenditure on the tuberculosis dispensary service in £s per case on the dispensary register in each borough in 1931; figures provided privately by the Comptroller of the London County Council.

m Percentage of occupied males aged 14 and over, engaged at the 1931 Census in the twelve occupations which had the highest mortality from pulmonary tuberculosis during 1930-32. Computed from Table 16 of the 1931 Census Occupation Tables, and Table R and Appendix C of the Registrar General's Decennial Supplement, 1931, Part IIa.

p Proportion of persons per 1,000 total population whose birthplace was shown as Ireland at the 1931 Census. Computed from Table 30, 1931 Census, General Tables, pp. 197 et seq.

o Major public open space and private open space, allotments and waterways per cent of total existing acreage as shown in London County Council Draft Development Plan, 1951. (This was the position before development and broadly indicated the open space existing for many years.)

Factors b, c, d were intended to measure social conditions and in addition it was considered that c would also measure the epidemiological influence of overcrowding apart from the economic conditions associated with poor housing conditions. The nutritional status of the boroughs was roughly indicated by f. Factors g and h were intended to measure the strength of the tuberculosis services. The occupational risk was intended to be indicated by m. Irish immigration could not be ignored and so factor p was introduced. Open spaces were referred to index o. Much of the information required for the calculation of the indices was only measured accurately at the Census of

10

1931, and it was for this reason that the analysis was based on the period 1931-33. Index f was based on 1938 because no other data were available, but it is not thought that at 1931 the borough pattern would have been different.

Social class (b), for example, was strongly correlated with housing (c), nutrition (f), occupation (m) and Irish birthplace (p). If therefore there was an association between tuberculosis mortality and Irish birth there would also apparently be an association between tuberculosis and social class. Which was the direct and which the indirect of the correlations? This question could be answered only by calculating the partial correlation coefficient between z and b, z and c, etc., while the influence of other factors is removed (the effect is as though, while z and b are considered, the other factors c, d, etc., are not allowed to vary among the boroughs and so cannot influence the direct association between z and b).

Table 2 gives values of the partial correlation coefficients found for the several multiple regression equations which were evolved.

In the analysis g and h were excluded owing to their lack of significance and d was omitted owing to its obvious overlap with b and c. The order of introduction of the factors was determined after experimentation with many combinations.

The second equation of Table 2 took into account the average social status of the borough and the average degree of mild crowding in dwellings – i.e., the combined effects of economic level and facilities for exposure in the home. The small increment in variance explained by c indicated that much of the "housing" effect had been stolen by "social class" simply because it was introduced first and was highly correlated with housing. Fairly strong association with these two factors *together* was demonstrated with a contribution of 58 per cent of sums of squares. In equation 3 the independent effect of nutrition (bodyweights of children) was introduced – i.e., the effect not already contained within social class and housing and "stolen" by those two factors – but no significant association existed and there was no further appreciable effect on the variance absorption. Equation 4 was a surprise, for the partial correlation coefficient for m was not significantly different from zero; on the other hand the consequent reduction in the partial coefficient for housing density suggested that the factor of employment in the specified occupations was not a direct tuberculosis risk so much as an association with the social background common to these low-grade occupations (c and m are highly correlated – see Table 1).

11

Table 2. Partial Correlation Coefficients between Tuberculosis Mortality 1931-33 and Factors Specified

Equation of Multiple Regression	b Social class (proportions in IV. V)	c Housing density (per cent living more than 1½ per room)	f Nutrition (mean weights per cent London average)	m Per cent in high mortality occupations	p Irish born proportion	o Open space (per cent of total borough area)
1.	+.73	—				—
2.	+.45	+.35	—			—
3.	+.44	+.32	−.022			—
4.	+.44	+.20	−.0048	−.047		—
5.	+.39	+.20	+.046	−.043	−.36	—
6.	+.36	+.18	+.040	−.042	−.34	−.019

Source of Variance		Sums of Squares	Degrees of Freedom
Variation explained by	b	.2994	1
Increment explained by addition of	c	.0325	1
	f	.0003	1
	m	.0007	1
	p	.0306	1
	o	.0415	1
Residual		.1653	21
		.5703	27

No.	Regression Equation
1.	$z = .0103b$
2.	$z = .0067b + .0044c$
3.	$z = .0067b + .0043c - .0020f$
4.	$z = .0067b + .0054c - .00045f - .0027m$
5.	$z = .0055b + .0050c + .0041f - .0023m - .0036p$
6.	$z = .0056b + .0048c + .0035f - .0022m - .0035p - .00024(o)$

Equation 5 showed that the introduction of the proportion Irish born produces a partial correlation coefficient of −.36, which is only just below the 5 per cent significance level. The negative sign of the correlation coefficient and the fact that the coefficient of correlation with social class was reduced to .39 indicated, however, that as suggested above, what was measured here was not an influence of place of birth so much as the influence of the social status of the borough. By the inclusion of o (Equation 6) the other coefficients for social class and housing, etc., were only slightly reduced, while the partial correlation coefficient for o was almost zero (compared with zero order −.296). This indicated also that o was not independent of b or c. It had to be borne in mind that those who lived in areas with little open space were commonly those who could not afford to live in better residential areas and could not afford good housing and other amenities.

The general conclusion to which these calculations led was that there was very little gain in introducing the factors other than social class and housing density. Clearly no new factors related to mortality which were independent of economic status had been revealed. (None of the partial correlation coefficients was large enough to be regarded as statistically significant.)

FACTOR ANALYSIS

This problem of measurement was crystallised by Buckatzsch (1947, no. 8) who emphasised that, as we have already seen, failing the possibility of observing "the response of suitably selected populations to artificially varied environments" it is necessary to analyse the mortality rates "actually recorded in various localities and at various times in terms of .... knowledge of the differences of environment in the localities concerned." He remarks that "the method is tantamount to regarding the death rates recorded in different areas at given times as the results of vast biological experiments performed impersonally by the operation of the social system in its progress through time." Buckatzsch proceeded to demonstrate the danger of accepting partial regression equations which owing to the non-independence of the "explanatory" factors are not really determinate, and do not really measure the relative strength of the number of factors employed. He also emphasised the important fact that the material "particularly that used to define the environmental conditions studied, consists of information collected for other, usually administrative, purposes and of only incidental relevance to the problems of social medicine." Buckatzsch recommended the use of factor analysis as a sharper tool to cut through the tangle of interdependence. Factor analysis does indeed achieve this limited objective but it leaves an even more difficult problem of interpretation; of attaching a real meaning to the separated factors. There is one extension of the classifying power of factor analysis which should be referred to, since it was indeed developed by Buckatzsch (1946, no. 7), that is the use of factor loadings as weights in the construction of a composite social index. To some extent this is making virtue out of necessity and admitting that it is not possible to take apart the whole interrelationship of elements that constitute the environment of man.

URBAN TYPOLOGY

That factor analysis is a powerful method of classification, Moser and Scott (1961, no. 13) have shown in their interesting study of urban typology in Britain.

Moser and Scott had the task of reducing a mosaic of urban complexes into some kind of order that would permit on the one hand of summary description of towns as groups and on the other of profitable study of factors influencing urban profiles. As we have already remarked they had to make the best of such statistics as were available from the census or from vital registration or other general sources. They assembled, for their main analysis some 57 variables. Seven of these covered sex, age and marital condition distribution; eight were concerned with population growth and birth rates; fifteen related to household size and housing conditions; fourteen variables covered industrial activity, occupational groupings, journey to work and retail sales; there were five voting statistics; six variables related to mortality or sickness; two were concerned with education. The central idea of the study was to unravel the *relationship* between a host of urban characteristics, and to measure them precisely, rather than to study in detail any single feature.

Any one of these indices could be used to group together towns, similar in this one respect, but this same grouping would mask implicit similarities in other respects because the variables were not independent of one another. If towns with high proportions of professional and managerial workers were selected they would tend also to be towns with low density housing, low infant mortality, high educational standards etc. Where the association between two indices was very strong then grouping by one would be the same as grouping by the other and, to say the least, it would have been a waste of time to carry out the procedure since the second exercise added no more information to the first. The problem was to find out how much really new information could be gleaned by referring to additional variables and in order to do this the degree of independence of variables or of groups of variables had to be ascertained. It would be much more economical and far less perplexing to classify on four or five really independent axes than to unravel a tangled skein of associations with a multiplicity of interrelated variables. But this ascertainment of independence of variables is the central problem, and where, as in this case, the variables are not tailor-made but have to be selected from a whole battery of available demographic indices then it is all the more essential.

The study by Moser and Scott covered 157 towns in England and Wales with populations in 1951 of 50,000 or more. They included all but three of the 80 County Boroughs, 64 Municipal Boroughs, 12 Urban Districts and the Administrative County of London, and in all they embraced slightly over half the population of England and Wales. It is important to remember that these are administrative areas. One great deficiency of British statistics is the lack of any statistics of towns as integral communities; that is, of the populations of distinct urban clusters of dwellings (street formations or scattered buildings which are not separated by more than a specified distance) representing localities or groups of people with a measure of social and economic interdependence in their daily lives. Such localities tend in their development to leave local authority boundaries behind and a single locality may sprawl across more than one local authority area. Even with a very rough identification of such urban clusters it was found at the 1951 Census of England and Wales that 320 local authority areas contained only 148 distinct communities in this sense. Here again therefore the statisticians have to make do with local authority areas since all census and vital registration statistics are based on these administrative units. All this injects heterogeneity into the picture and makes the tangled skein more tangled; for every town is on the average only half a community.

Taking towns as they found them and variables as they found them the authors attempted to "discern a systematic pattern for all, or groups of, towns both in the common and contrasting elements". They did this by component analysis, i.e. by recognising mathematically the most pronounced areas of overlap (components) and, within these areas, the most significantly contributing variables (to give a label to the component). Four main components were identified (1) social class (a term here reflecting all variables

15

obviously related to socio-economic conditions or occupational structure such as infant mortality, or educational attainment (2) population change between 1931 and 1951 (an index of age of the town) (3) population change between 1951 and 1958 (and index of recent development or redevelopment) (4) housing density (overcrowding, small houses, poor water supply etc.). These components were then used to classify the towns (number of towns in brackets) in the following scheme.

1. Mainly resorts, administrative and commercial
   (a) seaside resorts (10)
   (b) spas, professional and administrative centres (10)
   (c) commercial centres with some industry (16)

2. Mainly industrial towns
   (a) railway centres etc. (14)
   (b) ports etc. (10)
   (c) textile etc. (16)
   (d) north east seaboard, mining towns of Wales (11)
   (e) more recent metal manufacturing etc. (14)

3. Suburbs and suburban type
   (a) exclusive residential (9)
   (b) older type of mixed residential (12)
   (c) newer type of mixed residential (11)
   (d) including light industry (9)
   (e) older type working class and industrial type (10)
   (f) newer type of industrial (3)

4. Not allocated (2)

This classification was automatic. It was virtually made by the computer after the raw material of indices has been supplied to it; the criterion of classification (though not the labels) emerged from the analysis itself.

This, then, though in itself a major achievement of typology, is as far as factor analysis can take us. We are left with composite social indices, with little room for choice and only the possibility of using the factor analysis technique to assist the choice or to provide some system of weighting elements of a composite index.

16

If we are to be forced back upon rather general measures of social conditions, we come to a problem of growing importance but one that is slowly yielding to treatment – the measurement of levels of living.

Agencies responsible for applying economic aid to less developed countries have long felt the need for some measure not only of the absolute socio-economic conditions of populations, as a guide to priority for assistance, but also of changes in such conditions as an index of the efficacy of economic aid. As the primary international agency in this field the United Nations has concerned itself very much with this problem and has organized studies and conferences culminating in a report of a Committee of Experts convened by the Secretary General (1954, no. 16). The U.N. report, which has received further and developing study by international organisations, was couched in general terms. Since it was published Moser (1957, no. 12) has made an attempt to consider the problems in relation to a particular country – Jamaica.

It is a paradox that every social worker knows what he means by "standard of living" (and they probably all mean much the same thing) but as we have remarked no one can separate the whole complex of social conditions into essential, definable and measurable elements recognisable in every kind of society and comparable both from country to country and from period to period. The U.N. report proposed twelve components: health, food and nutrition, education, conditions of work, employment situation, aggregate consumption and savings, transportation, housing, clothing, recreation, social security, and human freedom. Moser chose to apply himself to education, nutrition, health and housing with some less detailed reference to income, expenditure and consumption; his description of the conceptual difficulties which he encountered in appraising the data available and of the way in which he formed a judgment of indicators represented a considerable practical advance.

Moser found it useful to classify indicators into three broad groups relating respectively to resources (schools, hospitals, etc.), utilisation of resources (school enrolment, hospital attendance, etc.) and the end-effects at which these resources are aimed (literacy rates, mortality rates, etc.). The case for and against a composite or summary indicator (to embody all indicators) was carefully argued. The conclusion was reached that it might be more meaningful to group the resources indices into a "social resources account"

17

and to assess the return obtained on these resources in terms of improved social conditions. There is clearly a wide field of research open here.

In the end Moser argued, as many others have argued, that "it is misleading to compare the level of living of two countries whose climate, laws, customs, values and social and economic structure differ in important respects". The proposed solution is to standardise each country's level of living by reference to its own target standard. The target standards are to be based on "needs" using "similar criteria". It would not be fair to expect a single exploration such as this to chart completely such a wide area of uncertainty, and further work is awaited. The approach has so far not been strictly applied to the study of mortality differentials and so we must leave the subject at this point. With the essential problems of measurement under scrutiny but still unsolved and with an admission of lack of precision and definition we turn to a consideration of observed social and economic differentials in mortality.

TIME CHANGES IN DEATH RATES

A possible if somewhat crude method of examining the influence of economic and social factors is simply to correlate changes in mortality over time with observed historical changes in the social situation or in public health activity. Thus Brown and McKeown (1955, no. 153) made an appraisal of the mortality changes in England and Wales in the eighteenth century and reached the conclusion that the decline in mortality was attributable much less to any medical advances than to improvements in environment even though this is in conflict with the view of some economic historians that on balance the economic and social changes of the industrial revolution were not favourable.

More recently McKeown and Record (1952, no. 154) have examined the reasons for the decline of mortality in England and Wales during the nineteenth century. Five diseases or disease groups accounted for almost the whole of the reduction in mortality between 1851-60 and 1891-1900: tuberculosis (all forms), 47.2 per cent; typhus, enteric fever and simple continued fever, 22.9 per cent; scarlet fever, 20.3 per cent; diarrhoea, dysentery and cholera, 8.9 per cent; and smallpox, 6.1 per cent. McKeown and Record conclude that, in order of their relative importance, the influences responsible for the decline were: (a) a rising level of living (especially improved diet) (b) hygienic changes introduced by the sanitary reformers and (c) a favourable trend in the relationship between infectious agent and human host. It is

18

alleged that the effect of therapy was restricted to smallpox and that it therefore had only a trivial effect on the total reduction in mortality. The method of study is not entirely satisfying since it assumes that what cannot be explained by preventive and curative therapy or genetic selection is *most probably* attributable to environmental influence though no specific influences are identified.

George Stolnitz (1955, no. 157), on the bases of a compilation of all national life tables on record, has looked at a whole century of international mortality trends and has attempted to summarise the chief generalisations that can be drawn. He has hypothecated that "the technical factors making for longer life by 1875 could be reinforced only to a secondary degree by rises in levels of living". His case is that "intensive investigation would probably reveal that the late nineteenth century upsurge in life chances occurred in the face of very substantial variations in economic levels and trends among the population of the West. The upsurge also coincided closely with the momentous discoveries of Pasteur and Koch, the first substantial spread of environmental sanitation, and the transition from fact-finding to effective implementation of public health programming. It also seems likely that urban-rural mortality differentials since 1875 have changed in a way which cannot be significantly explained by reference to new conditions in the general environment."

GENERATION MORTALITY STUDIES

Another way of attempting to separate the effects on mortality of social changes is to follow the changes in mortality of successive generations or cohorts. The normal life table confounds the experience of many different generations; the death rates in a single short period of time of two successive age groups are based on the deaths contributed in the short period by two generations born the same interval of time apart as that which separates the two age groups – the vertical columns of the diagram page 20.

If, however, a diagonal progression is followed then the experiences, in successive age groups, of the same generation are united. The differences between generation mortality tables calculated in this way help to bring into sharper relief those changes in mortality which have a "generation", though not necessarily genetic, origin. Derrick (1927, no. 152) plotted generation death rates and demonstrated (up to that time) consistent parallelism between

19

the curves. He stated that "the age factor in the determination of mortality has varied very little over the past 80 years, and .... nearly the whole of the temporal change is due to an entirely independent "generation" influence, each generation being endowed with a vitality peculiarly its own, which persistently manifests itself throughout the succeeding stages of its existence, determining the position of its mortality curve in relation to those of other generations, but not materially disturbing the shape of the mortality curve itself."

Period / Age	1901-5	1906-10	1911-15	1916-20	etc.
0-4					
5-9					
10-14					
15-19					
20-24					
etc.					

Point study — *Generation study*

Independently at the same time Davidson and Reid (1929, no. 149) developed a similar hypothesis though from a somewhat different standpoint. Adopting a Bayesion approach, they were concerned with the use of mortality rates of earlier experiences as a basis for a priori probabilities in the derivation of current mortality rates. In the choice of earlier rates they hypothecated greater consistency between rates in different periods of time but related to the same generation.

More recently Springett (1950, no. 156), Daw (1950, no. 150), and Spicer (1954, no. 155) in independent studies of tuberculosis mortality have shown how changes over time in the shape of the age curve of death rates from this disease, i.e. the tendency for the peak in mortality to move steadily to later ages and to become diminished, is due to succeeding generations having lower mortality. The residual (at later ages) of the high mortality of an early cohort is greater than the early adult peak of a recent generation. The early adult peak does, in fact, more truthfully reflect the natural history of the disease.

Beard (1963, no. 148) in a study of lung cancer mortality has taken this line of study a step further by moving from two to three dimensions or axes of presentation. He treats mortality as a stochastic process and derives logistic curves for the variation of mortality with age, part being variation of calendar

20

year of experience and part being variation of year of birth. Not only is a close fit to the actual death rates achieved but the variation associated with calendar year of experience is correlated with cigarette consumption. This is true for both sexes, i.e. the apparent difference in the experience of the two sexes indicated in earlier studies is removed.

It must not be imagined that generation studies effect a pure division between genetic or constitutional factors on the one hand and evironmental factors on the other. If there is some genetic development spread over a period of time then successive generations may all be affected in a varying degree; similarly a social change even if quite sharp will be lived through by a number of different generations though at different ages. Thus it may be that whichever form of mortality presentation is used – current or generation – only subtle differences in the mortality curves will remain to indicate whether genetic (and endogenous) or environmental (and exogenous) influences are operative.

NUTRITION

A great deal is now known about diseases arising from specific excesses or deficiencies in diet, and about the mortality that is likely to ensue. It is necessary to distinguish between a situation where as a result of lack of economic development or war or catastrophe supplies of food are generally scarce or of poor quality and a situation where food supplies are generally ample in quantity or quality but either because of poverty, ignorance or bad housekeeping (often engendered by bad housing) nutritional diseases arise.

The one grave economic factor in mortality to which we must give priority of consideration is the serious shortage of food in vast underdeveloped areas of the world. Sukhatme (1961, no. 42) has developed a method of estimating the incidence of hunger in the population, based on the international reference scale for calorie requirements and on the variation in energy expenditure among men of the reference age group. He has reached the conclusion that between 300 and 500 million people in the world are under-nourished. He has presented data on calorie consumption levels, region by region throughout the world, together with the corresponding requirements, and has drawn attention to the hunger gap of 11 per cent between the average levels of per caput consumption and requirement for the populous region of the Far East, and to the wide variation in calorie consumption levels between countries and between segments of the population within countries against

21

a relatively small variation in their calorie requirements. Apart from emphasizing the stark fact that between one third and one half of the world's population suffers from hunger and malnutrition Sukhatme makes a constructive estimate of the amount of foods needed for the world's growing population to eliminate the hunger gap. Food supplies will have to be more than doubled by 1980 and trebled by the turn of the century in order to bring about a moderate improvement in the level of nutrition of the people of the world. This problem of subnutrition is likely to be acute for some time to come. The following figures illustrate the mortality effects.

Current levels of calorie supplies as percentage of requirements (per caput per day at the retail level, taken from Sukhatme) and death rates per 1,000 (taken from *U.N. Demographic Year Book 1960)*, by regions,

	Calorie supplies as % of calorie requirements	Death rate, 1955-59 per 1,000
Far East	89	23
Near East	102	21
Africa	98	27
Latin America	102	19
Europe	115	10
North America	119	9
Oceania	125	9

The true mortality effects of food shortage are obscured by other causes of high mortality in tropical countries, e.g. malaria (though this is less important more than a decade ago) but the contrast between those regions of ample food supplies and those with little margin or actual scarcity is clear enough. Medical advances have made it possible to reduce the worst effects of qualitative deficiencies of food – beriberi, scurvy, pellagra – but sheer underfeeding cannot be combated by medical knowledge.

With this grim reminder of the greatest of all economic factors in mortality – lack of sustenance – we may turn to more specific aspects of nutrition in the context of the present review.

First the more overt deficiency conditions. Kwashiorkor is a disease of infants and young children weaned to a diet consisting of roots and cereals poor in protein. Many children, who suffer from it, die and those who survive may develop cirrhosis of the liver in later life. There are a large number of vitamin diseases. The more important in the context of this study are rickets (strictly due to lack of calcium but often due to lack of vitamin D which promotes absorption of calcium) resulting in bone deformity and a higher risk of respiratory disease; scurvy which is due to lack of ascorbic acid and if neglected may give rise to a risk of sudden heart failure; beriberi occurs among populations living mainly on polished rice or white wheaten flour with little green vegetable in the diet – it is a syndrome of two quite distinct disorders which may occur together but more often separately. "Wet" or cardiovascular beriberi is due to thiamine (vitamin B1) deficiency (which affects carbohydrate metabolism) and there is often also evidence of lack of protein, iron, vitamin A, nicotinic acid, and riboflavin. The result is cardiac embarrassment, dilatation and eventual failure. This form of disease seldom occurs in underfed people; indeed it may be associated with obesity. In contrast "dry" beriberi or nutritional polyneuropathy *is* associated with subnutrition; the disease is a symmetrical, bilateral, peripheral nerve degeneration leading to muscular wasting and loss of peripheral sensation. There is also pellagra, the disease affecting those who live on maize which is deficient in tryptopham a material needed for the synthesis of nicotinic acid in the body. In long standing cases of this disease there may be persistent mental, spinal cord and digestive disorders.

Clearly these diseases must be more prevalent in conditions of poverty and ignorance but as causes of mortality they have been virtually eradicated in most of those more developed countries from which alone there are good mortality statistics on which to base any study of social and economic differentials. In Japan in 1959 there were 447 deaths attributed to beriberi, 16 to pellagra, 16 to scurvy, 48 to active or late rickets, 6 to osteomalacia, and 911 to other avitaminoses and nutritional deficiency states (mostly "malnutrition" unqualified), out of a total of 689,959 deaths from all causes. These are relatively small numbers in terms of mortality risks. One assumes that the deaths occurred in the lower social strata but the published data are not sufficiently detailed to establish this. In England and Wales in 1960 there were 4 deaths from beriberi, none from pellagra, 2 from scurvy, none from rickets, 5 from osteomalacia and 96 from other nutritional deficiency states. These numbers would not sustain any study of differentials. Even if one goes back thirty years there are not enough deaths from these specific diseases to permit study of any social and economic factors involved.

It is even more difficult to assess the role of those nutritional deficiencies, most of them associated with adverse social conditions, that do not give rise to disabling symptoms but nevertheless result in a general lowering of

23

well-being. It is generally believed, for example, that, aside from the advent of new drugs and antibiotics, changes in the virulence of organisms, and advances in mass immunisation, some part of the dramatic reduction in mortality from infectious disease in children in Britain in the past thirty years can be attributed to improved resistance following a general rise in the nutritional level. During this period and especially during World War II considerable educational emphasis was placed upon balanced dietary while at the same time economic conditions improved with full employment and a diminution of wage differentials.

In surveys carried out in Britain prior to World War II Widdowson (1947, no. 43) showed that there was a wide variation as between the children of the "professional class" and those of the "artisan class" in the intake of ascorbic acid in particular, and generally also in the intake of fresh fruit and in the variety of diet, but these findings were not correlated with any measurements of disease incidence. The children of unemployed parents were found by Widdowson to be generally below the average of the other children both in height and weight. Their diets contained more bread but less milk and meat, and less of most of the dietary essentials. There is abundant evidence of the association between poorer social conditions and restricted physical growth of children both in height and weight (for example, Benjamin, 1953, no. 2, Miller et al., 1960, no. 124), but in so far as this is reflected in delayed attainment of maturity it could be argued, on the basis of animal and insect research showing association between restricted food intake, delayed maturity and longevity (Rockstein, 1959, no. 41), that this might mean prolonged survival. Here again we are prevented from making any specific assessment of the role of nutrition by the interference of other associations; nutritional deficiency is associated with relative poverty with which also is associated poor parental care, insanitary housing conditions, higher incidence of respiratory and other infections. The grossly undernourished die with specific signs of their dietary deficiency; the less obviously ill-nourished may die on this account alone more rapidly than their more fortunate fellows but the evidence is overlayed by the marks of other factors.

At the other end of the scale there is over-feeding and obesity. Here the picture is a little clearer. Excessive body weight subjects the cardiovascular system to excessive strain; in addition there is a specific association between obesity and diabetes mellitus. There are other physical consequences of excessive fat; bronchitis, abdominal hernia, gall-bladder disease, arthritis of the hips and knees, and restricted movement leading to higher risks of accidents. The experience of the Metropolitan Life Insurance Company (1951, no. 37) shows that male policyholders aged 20-64 and rated for over-weight suffered death rates 50 per cent above standard risks; for female policyholders of the same age range the excess was 47 per cent. The excess mortality was greater for the following causes: heart disease, cerebral haemorrhage, chronic nephritis, diabetes, cirrhosis of the liver, appendicitis, hernia, cancer of the gall-bladder, biliary calculi and other gall-bladder diseases, automobile accidents and accidental falls.

Though the relationship between obesity and mortality is thus clear, the operation of social and economic factors is not so clear. While there is considerable variation in metabolism and in activity between individuals so that one person would grow fat on a diet that would leave another person slim it remains true that for any one person obesity results from eating more calorific food than is consumed in activity. It is also true that overfeeding can be, and is, indulged in by those whose incomes permit it; that is by the rich rather than by the poor. However to the extent that poor people may substitute cheaper carbohydrates for dearer protein in their diets, obesity is often also associated with poverty. Dietary surveys carried out in Britain by the Ministry of Agriculture, Fisheries and Food (1959, no. 146) indicate the following distributions of sources of energy value for households graded by the occupational group of the head of the household (Table 3, p. 26).

It will be seen that classes IV and V have a greater proportionate contribution from carbohydrate than classes I and II and a smaller contribution from proteins.

Once again therefore we find a somewhat complicated situation in which affluence, by increasing total intake, and poverty, by affecting the dietary constituents of a lowered intake may both encourage the development of obesity.

OCCUPATION

It is now well recognised that the manner in which a man gains his livelihood and the surroundings in which he spends the greater part of his working hours must have an important influence upon his health. We have already indicated, however, that it is difficult to separate the influence of those elements of his environment which are directly associated with occupation as such from those of a more general character associated with his level of income.

Table 3. Percentage of Energy Value derived from Protein, Fat and Carbohydrate and of Protein from Animal Sources (per cent)

| | I Professional, etc. occupations | II Intermediate occupations | III Skilled Occupations | | | | IV Partly Skilled Occupations | | | | V | | All households |
			Mining manual workers	Other manual workers	Non-manual workers	All	Agricultural workers	Other manual workers	Non-manual workers	All	Un-skilled occupations	Not gainfully occupied	
Protein........	12.2	11.7	11.5	11.5	11.7	11.5	11.1	11.5	11.5	11.4	11.5	11.5	11.6
Fat	39.8	39.3	38.3	37.9	38.8	38.0	37.7	37.5	37.8	37.5	36.9	37.3	38.1
Carbohydrate .	48.0	49.0	50.2	50.7	49.5	50.4	51.2	51.0	50.7	51.1	51.6	51.2	50.3
Animal protein as percentage of total protein	64.0	60.7	54.1	56.9	59.7	57.3	54.9	55.4	55.9	55.3	55.2	57.0	57.6

Registrar-General's Social Classes

For a proper study of the mortality effect of occupation we need to know not only the number of deaths for each cause by age and sex in each occupation (if possible by duration of engagement in the occupation) but also the relative population at risk i.e. the average numbers engaged in the occupation similarly classified. On a national basis it is not practicable to attempt to obtain information of duration of engagement in the occupation either at a population census or at death registration. Details of occupation are recorded at the population census and, apart from the omission of the durational element, this enables populations at risk to be derived applicable to periods of time close to the census data. Occupation of the deceased is routinely furnished by the "informant" at death registration and it is customary for the registration authorities in several countries to tabulate this information for years surrounding the census, and to prepare reports on occupational mortality. For the most recent investigation in England and Wales (General Register Office, 1958, no. 53) the extended period 1949-53 was chosen to enable large numbers of deaths to be deployed; finer analysis could thus be made without diminishing the size of the groups to a point at which the rates became liable to relatively large chance errors.

AGE STANDARDISATION

It is essential in any comparative study of occupational mortality to standardise for age. A crude death rate based on the total population claiming a particular occupation would be liable to mislead in two ways:

(1) The death rate in occupation A might be higher than that in occupation B although age for age mortality is higher in B simply because, for example, B happened to be a more youthful population either by virtue of reduced longevity or because it comprised a new occupation of fairly recent recruitment. The following figures illustrate the first cause:

England and Wales
Average annual death rates per 1,000 living at each
age period 1910-12

	15-	20-	25-	35-	45-	55-	65-74	All ages 15-74
Farmers	0.5	1.5	3.1	4.6	8.6	20.0	51.3	11.6
Coal miners (hewers and getters)	3.2	3.8	4.4	6.7	12.7	30.1	82.3	9.3

The death rates at each age were higher for coal miners but owing to the fact that the fewer survived to older ages they were a younger population than farmers and so experienced a lower crude death rate (the crude death rate is a weighted average of the age specific rates in which the weights are the populations in each age group actually in the population studied).

(2) The total population claiming a particular occupation will include some too young to have incurred any real measure of occupational risk and many too old to have had any contact with the occupational hazard for many years prior to death (though to exclude them would lessen the weight given to any postponed effects). In addition, statements of occupation are particularly liable to be misleading for older persons who may refer to an occupation from which they retired early in life (e.g. police) or to one to which they have only recently entered as an adaptation to physical disability gained in an earlier occupation.

It is therefore usual in the investigations carried out by the Registrar General of England and Wales to restrict consideration to the occupied and retired population of ages 20-65 (with subsidiary examination of the 35-65 group) and to allow for varying age structure within the range by standardisation. Separate examination is made of males, single women and married women. The married women are classified by the occupation of their husbands. This is to provide a means of obtaining an indication of real occupational factors. If the wives show the same excess mortality as the husbands for a particular occupation it is implicit that a general environment or socio-economic factor is involved rather than a true occupational hazard. Two methods of age standardisation have been used.

(1) For each occupation a standard population is chosen of the same age distribution as that of the whole census population of the particular group considered (all males, single women or married women) but reduced in total size so that it yields 1,000 deaths when the "all cause" age specific rates for all males (or single women etc.) are applied to it. Applying the *actual* age specific rates for the occupation gives an index called the "comparative mortality figure" (C.M.F.) which is in fact the ratio of "actual" to "expected" deaths (where "expected" means expected on the basis of "all males" mortality) in a population of *standard* structure. This method was last employed in the Report associated with the 1921 Census.

(2) Age specific rates based on all males (or single women etc.) are applied to the census population for the occupation to give a figure of "standard" deaths and the actual deaths are expressed as a ratio (called the "standardised

28

mortality ratio" (S.M.R.)) to the "standard" deaths. This index is a ratio of "actual" to "expected" in a population not of standard structure but of a structure typical of the occupation. This method was used in the investigations associated with the censuses of 1931 and 1951. These operations are performed separately over the range 20-65 and 35-65.

The two indices described above are normally almost equal, but if the excess mortality is concentrated at the ages where the occupation has relatively greater numbers (than in the all males distribution) the S.M.R.gives more emphasis to this excess than the C.M.F.; on the other hand, the C.M.F. is affected by random errors in those age rates of mortality for the particular occupation which are based on small numbers – in the S.M.R. they get only the representation of the small numbers actually at risk but in the C.M.F. they get the full representation of the standard population e.g. in 1930-32 engine drivers at risk at ages 20-35 formed only 7 per cent of the total at 20-65 compared with 42 per cent in the standard population and the C.M.F. was inflated by high apparent mortality at young ages based on small numbers and suspected of error from faulty occupational description at death registration. On balance the S.M.R. is normally adopted since the greater ease with which it can be computed (on a mass scale) outweighs the risk of minor anomalies.

DIFFICULTIES OF INTERPRETATION

The interpretation of occupational mortality data is much more difficult than the mere calculation of the indices, complicated though these may appear.

Occasional vagueness in the entry of occupation in census returns and death registers places a strain upon the capacity of the coding clerk to make a "reproducible" assignment to an occupation unit, i.e., an assignment that would be made by any other coder faced with the same description; there is thus no guarantee that in such circumstances the same assignment would be made for the same person at census and at death. Nor is it certain that in cases of death soon after the census date the same description will be used since the informant may refer to the occupation carried out for the greater part of the lifetime of the deceased rather than to the occupation in which the deceased was most recently engaged. For example a police sergeant who retires comparatively early in life may take up a clerical occupation of a relatively minor character to supplement his pension and give him an active interest; at his death it is very likely that the widow or other relative will still consider him to be a "retired police sergeant".

There is also a natural tendency for a householder completing a census schedule to elevate the status of his occupation, and for relatives to do the same at the registration of his death. This may take the form of using a description which implies a higher degree of skill or of supervisory capacity than is in fact applicable. If there were the same degree of elevation at both census and death registration there would be errors in the statistics of an absolute character but differentials would not be distorted. However, it has been found that the conditions under which the census is carried out – the prior propaganda, the instructions and examples on the census schedule, the fact that the occupation entry is only part of a more extended discipline (including reference to industry and workplace) – tend to make the census occupation entries more accurate than those made at registration.

An examination of discrepancies between occupational description of the same individuals at the census and at subsequent death registration was made in connection with the 1951 population census of England and Wales (General Register Office, 1958, no. 48). The census was held on 8th April, 1951. The registration entries relating to the deaths occurring in the first week of May were extracted. These deaths occurred sufficiently soon after the census to render a change of home address between enumeration and death unlikely, yet sufficiently long after the census to make it probable that the deceased were enumerated at their usual home address and not in hospital. It was therefore possible to match the census schedule and the information obtained at death registration. In particular the occupational description given by the deceased was compared with that furnished by a relative or other informant after his death. A total of 9,864 deaths were extracted and of these there were 892 for which the place of enumeration or circumstances at census date were such that the death entry did not furnish sufficient information to enable the census schedule to be traced (this number included 22 males and 17 females born since census day); there were also 449 cases where the schedule could be found but identification of the individual could not be made or was uncertain. There were a further 198 cases (111 males, 87 females) where a schedule was traced but the record indicated that the deaths related to infants born after census day. The following statement summarises the results of the comparison of the occupations of the 4,051 males in the sample:

30

	Age at census					
	16-34	35-54	55-64	65 and over	All ages	
					Number	Per cent.
Social class differs (a)	15	112	150	485	762	19
Socio-economic group differs (b)	17	131	179	578	905	22
Order differs (c)	12	104	180	494	790	20
Sub-order differs	3	13	22	45	83	2
Unit differs	9	64	66	275	414	10
One n.s. or no occupation	6	18	40	422	486	12
Total agreed (d)	61	352	463	1,402	2,278	56
Total matched	91	551	771	2,638	4,051	100

(a) The occupations were split into 5 social classes, viz., I Professional and managerial, II Intermediate, III Skilled workers, IV Intermediate, V Unskilled workers.

(b) There were 12 socio-economic groups. (1) Farmers, (2) Agricultural workers, (3) Higher administrative etc. (4) Other administrative etc. (5) Shopkeepers, (6) Clerical workers, (7) Shop assistants, (8) Personal service, (9) Foremen, (10) Skilled workers, (11) Semiskilled workers, (12) Unskilled workers.

(c) There were 28 Orders, 64 Sub-orders, and 583 units in the classification of occupations.

(d) Including those agreed as being unoccupied.

These discrepancies though serious in individual cases fortunately did not result in substantial net errors in the main occupational distributions used to provide populations for death rates at least for broad occupational groups. In most cases it was clear that the same occupational description was being attempted in terms which were not identical and that excessive specificity in the 1951 classification of occupations rendered coding vulnerable to the chance inclusion or exclusion of particular words in the job description. As a result the 600 units of the 1951 classification were telescoped into 200 units for the 1961 census with an improvement in coding precision. The absolute degree of error is greater at the older ages beyond retirement and less at working ages and the situation in Great Britain may generally be summarised by saying that the status of the occupation is slightly exaggerated at the census, is rather more exaggerated at death registration, but that the resultant bias in the direction of raising mortality in the higher grade occupations is not, for the ages for which indices are usually calculated, of serious consequence.

If it is thought that the net result of discrepancies between the information source of the numerator of the death rate (the death registration) and that of the denominator of the death rate (the census record) is likely to be important, these can be eliminated by carrying out a matching of the two records prior to the calculation of the specific occupational death rates. This is being done in the United States of America (Hauser and Kitagawa, 1961, no. 48) in connection with the occupational mortality investigation associated with the 1960 population census. However, such an operation is expensive since in order to permit analysis in specific occupation groups, a large number of deaths (500,000 in the U.S. investigation) has to be matched. Bearing in mind that, for reasons given below, this type of investigation is only a crude instrument for detecting occupational risks and that, for broad socio-economic comparisons, the errors are not so important, this degree of refinement would usually have to be weighed very carefully against other demands upon statistical resources.

The studies of occupational mortality are also handicapped by the fact that the information both at census and at death is related in most cases to the immediately antecedent occupation. While the census information probably gives a fair approximation to the mean numbers at risk in the different occupations the deaths will be biased in the direction of lighter occupations to the extent to which failing health may lead workers to foresake heavier for lighter employment. For example, the high mortality apparently associated with such occupations as machine minding, basket-making, or newspaper-selling, is probably entirely due to this factor of self-selection; these lighter occupations being taken up as an adaptation to pre-existing chronic illness or disability or to illness emerging during a prior and more strenuous occupation. The extent of this error is not known; it is probably corrected to some extent by a tendency, noted above, to refer back to the occupation with which the deceased was associated for most of his life. Ideally, deaths and numbers at risk would be classified by duration of employment but the difficulties of obtaining accurate information even at the census, let alone at death registration, are too great to be overcome with present resources.

Finally, reference has already been made to the difficulty of deciding whether excess mortality is due to occupational risk or general social environment and of the use, for example, of the mortality of wives as a control. The mortality index even thus controlled can do no more than establish a prima facie case for closer study within the particular occupation.

Having regard to these difficulties it must be appreciated that the occupational mortality investigation associated with the census is a very crude diagnostic tool, giving no exact or final answers but throwing into relief differentials worthy of closer study by more precise methods. In this way the investigations have proved of great value in the past. It is probable that, in the future, longitudinal studies (viz., following up groups of workers throughout their period of employment) in particular industries under the close supervision of medical field worders will be more efficient in revealing true occupational risks. Such studies would not be confined to mortality risks but would embrace also sickness absence, i.e., they would begin at a point nearer the onset of the occupational influence on health. We return to this subject later on.

OCCUPATIONAL DIFFERENCES

The occupations with the 20 highest Standard Mortality Ratios (all causes) among 425 occupational groups in the 1949-53 investigation in England and Wales are listed in the statement on p. 34.

Occupations with low mortality included, for example, Farmers, farm managers (S.M.R. of ma les20-64, 70), Foremen, overlookers in metal manufacture and engineering (68), Civil Service higher officers (60), Heads or Managers of Office Departments (55), Bankers, bank managers, inspectors (76), Teachers (not music) (66), Costing and Accounting Clerks (70).

For many occupations with low mortality the Standard Mortality Ratios for the wives were also low, e.g., Bankers, bank and insurance managers, etc., (husbands 78, wives 82), Teachers (husbands 66, wives 77), Clergymen of the Church of England (husbands 81, wives 80) indicating that it was not so much the occupation that was healthy as the level of living associated with the occupation. A similar argument (in the opposite direction) could be extended to some of the high mortality occupations in the 1949-53 analysis, e.g., the S.M.R. for the wives of drivers of horsedrawn vehicles (170), Furnacemen, kilnmen in chemical trades (164), Labourers (172), but in some instances there was a much greater excess mortality in husbands than in wives, e.g.,

	Husbands S.M.R.	Wives S.M.R.
173	Sandblasters	96
189	Glass blowers	133
160	Machine minders	123
150	Publicans, etc.	116

and this kind of contrast helps to establish prima facie evidence for closer enquiry.

High mortality occupations	S.M.R. 20-64 of men	S.M.R. 20-64 of wives (where given)
Royal Navy – other ranks – retired	826	—
Army – other ranks – retired	556	—
Royal Air Force – other ranks – retired	485	—
Slate workers (n.e.s.); slate masons	467	300
Tunnel miners	225	(50)
Getters (mines) (not coal)	222	149
Armed forces – commissioned officers – retired	189	—
Makers of glass and glassware – blowers (not machine hands or bench glass workers)	189	133
Drivers of horse drawn vehicles	189	170
Labourers and other unskilled workers in – All other industrial and commercial undertakings	186	172
Haulage contractors and managers	175	168
Sand blasters (excluding shot blasters)	173	96
Machine minders – others	160	123
Managers (n.e.s.)	155	—
Workers in chemical and allied trades - Furnacemen, kilnmen	154	164
In coal mines – Hewers and getters (by hand) – below ground	153	146
Land agents, estate agents	150	165
Publicans, owners, etc., of hotels, inns	150	116
Curriers, leather dressers	149	135
Coal mines – coal face coal getters, loaders	148	143

The main specifically occupational differentials emerging from the 1949-53 investigation were: a suggestion that some professional workers and farmers were at greater risk of death from poliomyelitis; sedentary workers had a higher death rate from coronary heart disease; a higher risk of pneumoconiosis, or respiratory tuberculosis with occupational disease of the lung in coal and other mining and quarrying, brickmaking and pottery, cotton strippers, and sandblasters; a higher mortality from cirrhosis of the liver in several occupations connected with the sale of alcoholic drinks (proprietors and managers of hotels, publicans, etc.); higher mortality from motor vehicle accidents among transport workers; higher mortality from other accidents among certain obviously hazardous occupations, for example, miners, steel erectors, window cleaners, railway platelayers.

Other occupational risks have emerged from specific investigations. For example in the study of carcinogens certain occupational associations have been found. The high incidence of skin epithelioma in cotton mule spinners in Britain nearly forty years ago led to investigations which corroborated the suspicion that the lubricating oil used was carcinogenic and this was followed by protective action, viz., the use of oils of different composition and modification of machinery to prevent oil splash. Cancer of the scrotum was at one time prevalent in chimney sweeps due to concentration of soot on the skin (one clear example of the value of soap and water – as Clemmesen (1951, no. 47) remarked "the Danish Chimney Sweepers Guild which in 1778 ruled that journeymen and their apprentices should have a daily bath, may, whatever their motives, have done more to prevent human cancer than many research workers"). Tumours of the urinary bladder in certain sections of the chemical industry (Case, Hosker, McDonald and Pearson, 1954, no. 46) have been found to be associated with specific aromatic hydrocarbons – in one important instance the isolation of the agent, an antioxident used in the rubber industry, led to its immediate voluntary withdrawal and the cessation of its manufacture (Case, Hosker, 1954, no. 45) but in other instances too there has been modification of handling processes or abandonment of production as a result of these clear statistical analyses. Another example is provided by the high incidence of lung cancer in those working with arsenic, asbestos dust (Perry, 1947, no. 52) or chromate dust (Brinton, Frasier and Kovan, 1952, no. 44).

URBANISATION

One of the strongest influences militating against health in the past has been the increasing gravitation of the population into crowded cities. By 1851 above half the population of England and Wales had become aggregated in towns. In 1921 only 20.7 per cent of the population was left in rural districts and in 1961 this proportion had fallen slightly to 20.0 per cent. In 1961 two-fifths of the population were concentrated in the six major conurbations* (the term given to certain large agglomerations of urban areas which represent towns that have outgrown their administrative boundaries). In earlier days, when the process of town expansion was not accompanied by the provision of public health or other environmental services as we now know them, town life was associated with many inimical factors – streets instead of fields; damp, dark and ill-ventilated dwellings instead of country cottages; dust and belching smoke and noise instead of sunshine and clean air and quiet; a preponderance of indoor occupations; crowding together of the population with enhanced opportunities for the transmission of infectious disease; bad drainage and risks of contamination of water supplies; importation of food from areas far distant from sources of supply with consequently increased opportunities for its infection and decay. Many of the worst elements of town life have been removed or mitigated by enlightened local government and by the general rise in standards of hygiene in the day to day life of the community at large. Many town dwellings are superior in space, heating ventilation and sanitation to the country cottage. The town often has the advantage of more extensive medical services. Indoor occupations still predominate but factory and office conditions are immeasurably better. The smoke and the noise and the herding together remain however; and if modern medicine and improved nutrition have together greatly lessened the mortality from infectious disease, more rapid and more voluminous traffic has not only increased the speed with which epidemics spread within a town from one town to another, but provided greater opportunities for fatal accidents.

That the urban differential in mortality still exists may be seen from the following age-standardised death rates per 1,000 in 1960, in England and Wales.

Conurbations and urban areas with population of 100,000 and over   12.4
Other urban areas 12.1
Rural districts 11.0

There has been some controversy as to whether there is any direct relationship between mortality and density of population as such when measured,

* Tyneside, West Yorkshire, South East Lancashire, Merseyside, West Midlands, Greater London.

36

for example, by the number of persons per square mile of the area in which they are resident. Farr (1843, no. 25) found an approximate arithmetical equality between the ratio of the death rates of two areas and the sixth root of the density of the population but he himself was doubtful of any implied law. Newsholme (1891, no. 26) himself showed that the relationship did not provide a basis for predicting the mortality in large tenement blocks. It has since become abundantly clear that the higher mortality springs not simply from the closeness with which people live together but from a whole complex of social and economic factors which may be associated with such crowding.

Local authorities in many countries have done much, especially in areas of new development to produce high quality housing in pleasant and open surroundings. The schoolroom and the workshop alike are now planned to provide the most comfortable conditions possible. However it still remains true that health is related not only to bricks and mortar and to medical services but is also dependent on mode of occupation and personal habits (in turn determined by intelligence and educational background) and nutrition; the level of living is associated with the level of income however much the strength of this association may be weakened by positive social security measures. We are brought to our problem of trying to disentangle the separate influence of particular elements in the general complex of social conditions when these elements are all interdependent. Those who can afford an expensive house can also afford to be well fed, and well clothed and by the same token are rarely in dirty or unhealthy occupations; they are usually well educated and know how to take care of their health. One condition implies all the others.

HOUSING

In so far as housing conditions *do* directly affect health, they normally do so by affecting the incidence of infectious disease. The more a household (of a particular size) is crowded into small or few rooms the greater the opportunity for infection to spread by droplet or direct contact from one to the other. This increase in the facility of transmission of infection is even greater when bedrooms have to be shared by members of the same family or where rooms are used both for living and sleeping; it is also greater, especially for diarrhoeal diseases, where more than one family are compelled to share the same sanitary arrangements (water closets or washing up facilities).

The important statistics to be measured are, in respect of each household –

Number of persons – under 15
            – 15 and over ⎤ giving persons per room
Number of rooms – living ⎟ as an index of crowding.
            – sleeping ⎦
Number of rooms used for sleeping by more than one person
Use of water closet – sole or shared
Use of washing up facilities – sole or shared.

CLASSIFICATION OF HOUSING CONDITIONS

There have been several attempts to reduce the several aspects of housng conditions that have to be taken into account in any general evaluation into a single figure index. This is done by awarding "points" or "scores" to the various aspects and adding up the total score. Stewart (1952, no. 35) used the following handicap rating for household amenities which, it will be noted, took account also of the domestic situation as indicated by reference to material commitments:

Handicap rating for household amenities

		Score
A.	Household Equipment	
	House condemned	5
	House damp	3
	Lavatory outside	3
	No mains water	3
	No piped hot water	3
	No garden	3
	No bathroom	3
B.	Density of Occupation (persons/rooms)	
	Greater than 1.5	13
	1.5 – 1.1	10
	Equal to 1	7
	0.9 – 0.8	4
	Less than 0.8	0
C.	Mother's Commitments	
	Household includes lodgers, paying guests, etc.	2

No domestic help   2
Older children under 10 years (a):
3 or more   9
2 or more   6
1 or more   3

(a) This index was used for child surveys and "older" means older than the child in the survey.

An index more strictly related to housing was evolved by Chapman and known as the Liverpool Housing Index (Barber and Blaschko, 1954, no. 28):

Liverpool housing index

1. Address

2. Age of house
   Pre-1918 1
   1918-1939 2
   Post-1939 3

3. House Owned by:
   Occupier 1
   Private owner 2
   Local authority 3
   Employer 4

4. Number of Separate Households
   1, 2, 3, 4

5. Number of Habitable Rooms
   Total rooms
   1, 2, 3, 4, 5, 6, 7, 8
   Bedrooms
   1, 2, 3, 4, 5, 6
   Other rooms
   1, 2, 3, 4, 5, 6

6. Structure	Code	Score
Flat – with lift frame construction	1	10
Others	2	12
Flat – without lift frame construction	3	5
Others	4	7
Terraced	5	6
Semi-detached	6	13
Detached	7	15

7. Paintwork		
Good condition	1	10
Fair condition	2	6
Bad condition	3	0

8. Rendering or Brickwork
   (A) *Rendering*

Good condition	1	10
Fair condition	2	6
Bad condition	3	0
Does not apply	4	

39

(B) *Brickwork & Pointing*

(i) *Brickwork*

Good condition	1	5
Fair condition	2	3
Bad condition	3	0
Does not apply	4	

(ii) *Pointing*

Good condition	1	5
Fair condition	2	3
Bad condition	3	0
Does not apply	4	

Note. Score for alternatives (A) or (B) but not for both.

9. Rooms

	Code	Score
Separate kitchen	1	9

1 living room	2	0
2 living rooms	3	6
3 living rooms or more	4	9

10. Water Supply

Inside piped supply and hot water system	1	23
Inside piped supply and one geyser	2	14
Inside piped supply, cold water only	3	6
Outside tap, well or pump	4	0

11. Lighting

Electricity	1	8
Gas	2	5
Other types	3	0

12. Daylight Obstruction

	1
	2
	3

13. Size of Largest Living Room

Under 100 sq. ft.	1	0
100-149 sq. ft.	2	2
150-199 sq. ft.	3	5
200-249 sq. ft.	4	7
250-299 sq. ft.	5	9
300 sq. ft. and over	6	10

House Score

Crowding

14. Households per Dwelling

1 household	1	8
2 or more households	2	0

Note: For number of households refer to Item 4.

15. Crowding Score

Total Index Score
(House & Crowding)

Unlike the previous index a high score on the Liverpool index indicates good housing. It has been found, as would be expected, that the scoring on this index is highly correlated with income.

The immediate difficulty is that while the population, which forms the denominator of the death rate may be classified according to these housing characteristics at the population census, it is not possible to enquire about housing conditions when deaths are registered and so the enumerators of death rates specific to housing differentials cannot be directly determined. We are therefore forced back once again to the device of isolating populations each sufficiently homogeneous in relation to a particular level of housing conditions and comparing the death rates.

There is also the difficulty, to which reference has already been made, of isolating the effect of housing conditions from that of other factors with which housing conditions are highly correlated. We have already reviewed one such enquiry in detail (Benjamin, 1953, no. 2), which showed that there was such an independent effect though not a powerful one – after social class (which absorbed 52 per cent of the inter-area variance), housing explained only a further 6 per cent of the variance. In a similar investigation in Glasgow, Stein (1952, no. 34), placed greater emphasis on overcrowding in housing accommodation, though here again it was difficult to distinguish the effect of housing from that of other factors, for example unemployment, which were brought into the analysis. Both these studies were related to tuberculosis. An earlier investigation relating to respiratory disease was equivocal (Smith, 1934, no. 33): a greater morbidity was found on new estates but among the rehoused group there was more unemployment. With regard to rheumatic conditions there have often been suggestions that dampness was a factor but Kellgren and others (1953, no. 31), could find no evidence that damp housing conditions greatly affected incidence and Hewitt and Stewart (1952, no. 30), found no evidence that rheumatism was associated with either bad housing conditions or with poverty as such. As we have already indicated, mortality from infectious disease is related to housing, especially among children. In a review in 1937 it was shown that mortality, particularly at ages 1-2 was closely associated with density of housing.

There are ad hoc investigations which are of value. It is often possible in enquiries into local outbreaks of infectious disease, for health visitors or sanitary inspectors to investigate such conditions by house to house enquiry both of the dwellings where cases of disease have occurred and, for purposes of estimating differential incidence, of a representative sample of *all* dwellings. For example in a study of the incidence of enteritis in London (Scott, 1953, no. 32), it was found that the housing density (persons per room) was

41

higher (2.05) in infected houses than in the survey area as a whole (1.38). Infants without any sign of diarrhoea, i.e. with much less evidence of infection, came from less crowded houses than those with diarrhoea. As compared with uninfected households, those with cases of enteritis had a higher incidence of sharing washing up facilities and of sharing water closets.

Again in an enquiry in a London Borough into the housing conditions of families in which a case of tuberculosis had been notified (Chalke, 1953, no. 29) it was found that in those households possessing sufficient accommodation for the tuberculous patient to have a *separate bedroom* the incidence of secondary cases was 5.7 per cent compared with 9.9 per cent in households where a separate bedroom could not be provided.

We are left with the reasonable conclusion that the direct effect of bad housing conditions (as distinct from the general level of living) upon mortality is only demonstrable in infectious disease, especially tuberculosis.

MARRIAGE

Marital condition is related to the mortality for certain causes – arising partly from the selective force of marriage itself, partly also because the contentment and happiness of married life (as well as the protection and discipline) are favourable to well-being and partly (in specific causes for women) from sexual expression, pregnancy and childbirth. For example, it has long been known that carcinoma of the breast, corpus uteri and ovary is commoner among single women while carcinoma of cervix uteri is commoner among married women and among those who have been married.

As illustration of what is meant by the reference to "discipline" we may note that a man who is suffering from a chronic disease is more likely to follow a necessarily strict regime if he has a wife to encourage him and to make it easy for him to do so. It is hardly possible to isolate the separate effects of marital selection, (the less fit being less inclined or finding it more difficult to find partners) and of marriage itself. As proof of the selective force of marriage it should be noted that married women's mortality is generally lighter than that of single women (except at advanced ages) and that an exceptional rise in marriage rates as after World War II, with many "marginal" marriages of spinsters who would not normally marry, tends to increase the mortality of married women as a whole.

The general picture is indicated by the following statement which shows the death rates per thousand living by sex, age and marital condition in 1959 in England and Wales:

42

MALES				Age-group	FEMALES			
Total	Single	Married	Widowed and Divorced		Total	Single	Married	Widowed and Divorced
12.3	4.10	14.1	81.6	All ages	11.0	5.47	6.61	49.0
2.33	2.33	—	—	0-	1.83	1.83	—	—
1.01	1.06	0.74	1.58	15-	0.44	0.45	0.43	0.79
1.12	1.76	0.91	1.64	25-	0.79	1.40	0.69	1.17
2.41	4.36	2.15	3.16	35-	1.78	3.07	1.60	2.63
7.22	10.4	6.81	10.4	45-	4.36	5.50	4.06	5.60
21.8	28.2	20.7	30.3	55-	10.8	12.1	9.97	12.6
53.6	57.5	49.7	71.7	65-	30.5	31.1	27.4	33.5
138	117	117	171	75 and over	106	110	76.2	115

At all the adult ages shown and for both sexes the mortality of the married is lower than that of the single. The excess tends to decrease with advancing age for both sexes, and at most ages is greater for men than for women. The greater excess at young ages may be due to the fact that the additive effect of selection is maximal at the modal marriage ages. It will also be noticed that for both sexes the mortality of the widowed and divorced tends to be higher than that of the single except at ages 25-44; at all ages their mortality is higher than that of the married.

The analysis of these differentials (General Register Office, 1961, no. 57) reveals that they are attributable to particular causes. Tuberculosis is higher among single than among married persons; here both selection for marriage and the less protective conditions of single life play a part. For the same reasons mortality from poliomyelitis and from chronic rheumatic heart disease is higher in single persons. Certain cancer differences for women have already been cited. There are others. Cancer of the stomach is less often found in single persons but they have a higher mortality from cancer of the oesophagus. Cancer of the buccal cavity, pharynx and larynx is more common among single males, a tendency which single females do not share. Mortality from cancer of the prostate is higher in single men than in married men. Fibromyata and benign ovarian tumors are more often a cause of death in single than in married women. Deaths from thyrotoxicosis are rare among males but the single are more affected than the married. Two disease groups with very small numbers of deaths are iron deficiency anaemias and presenile psychosis but in both cases there is an excess among single persons. It should be noted that presenile psychosis is the result of organic brain disease which does not usually make its appearance before the age of 40. Diseases of veins cause higher mortality among single persons. This group of diseases includes thrombo-phlebitis and various thromboses and pulmonary embolism and it is possible that the higher mortality might arise from the poorer nursing that these persons get at home when they are ill.

CLIMATE AND GEOGRAPHY

The influence of climate can only be separated with difficulty from that of other conditions of environment. No useful comparison bearing on this point can be made between the general death rate of communities possessing fairly good vital statistics but living in different climates. Australia, New Zealand, South Africa and Canada all furnish instances of remarkably low death rates associated sometimes with sub-tropical summers and extremely cold winters. Where a country is notoriously unhealthy this is usually due in a large measure to the endemicity of malaria or of other insect-borne diseases often along with parasitic diseases, e.g., anchylostomiasis. These causes can be removed and are being removed.

Climate has a marked influence on the prevalence of particular diseases, e.g., malaria or yellow fever where a high temperature is needed for effective multiplication of the vectors of infection. Diphtheria and scarlet fever prevail little in tropical countries. The prevalence of tuberculosis in some tropical areas is not a product of the climate but of other social factors coupled with racial susceptibility or lack of immunological protection. The common cold and influenza are found the world over but respiratory disease other than tuberculosis is not prevalent in dry sunny climates.

On the narrower question of geographical or regional variation in mortality within national boundaries the following exercise may provide a warning against taking such variation too much at its face value. Within England and Wales it has been shown (General Register Office, 1955, no. 22), that "levels of mortality (standardized for sex and age) tend to arrange themselves into three broad bands that run across the country from south west to north east. The highest levels of mortality are found in most of Wales and in the northern counties of England. Counties with intermediate levels of mortality, both in their urban and their rural components, are distributed in a line running from Cornwall northwestwards through the

Midlands and on towards the Humber and the Wash. The third area, of low mortality, starts on the south coast at Dorsetshire and likewise runs north west to include the home counties and continues on towards East Anglia". It might be thought that this mortality gradient is a purely geographical or climatic variation. Analysis soon shows that the social and economic factors are probably more important.

The following figures are taken from the Statistical Review for England and Wales for 1950, Text Volume:

1951 Census data

Standard Regions	Persons per room			Per cent of males 15 and over (occupied and retired) in Social Classes IV and V
	Urban areas of 50,000 or more population	Other urban areas	Rural areas	
Northern	0.85	0.85	0.78	33.9
East and West Ridings	0.74	0.75	0.74	31.6
North Western	0.74	0.72	0.71	31.0
Wales	0.74	0.70	0.72	34.2
North Midland	0.71	0.70	0.70	30.9
Midland	0.79	0.72	0.74	28.9
Eastern	0.70	0.69	0.67	29.1
London and South Eastern	0.68	0.66	0.65	24.6
Southern	0.71	0.67	0.70	26.1
South Western	0.73	0.65	0.68	27.6

These figures suggest that the higher mortality of the northern areas is associated with greater housing density and less favourable socio-economic conditions, though account must also be taken of the diminished sunlight and greater atmospheric pollution of the industrial north.

Once again it may be suggested that some factorial design is needed to analyse these variations satisfactorily. Categories of various factors would be defined, e.g., housing, socio-economic groups, urbanisation, atmospheric pollution, etc., and a selection of local areas would be made such that there would be a number fitting (i.e., roughly homogeneous in respect of) every cross-combination of these classifications. The mortality variance of these areas could then be analysed to show the relative weight and interdependence of the factors.

We digress now to consider certain factors which are particularly relevant to foetal mortality or to mortality of very early infancy. In an important series of papers (Heady, Daly and Morris, 1955, no. 82) giving the results of comprehensive studies carried out in England and Wales by the Medical Research Council Social Medicine Unit (with the help of the General Register Office) it has been demonstrated that the stillbirth rate rises with age for mothers of a particular parity while the post-neonatal rate decreases with age (except for mothers over 35). The stillbirth rate for mothers of a given age is high for first births, falls for second and third births, and rises thereafter; the post-neonatal rate for mothers of a given age, rises steadily with increasing parity. The neonatal rate varies less than the other two rates and appears to occupy an intermediate position. These results indicate, for post-neonatal mortality, the increased opportunity for infection (the principal cause) in larger families and the strain on economic resources and parental care of the larger family. Three "vulnerable" groups are picked out –

1. Mothers over 35, bearing first babies have a high risk of stillbirth.
2. Mothers over 40 of any parity have a high risk of stillbirth.
3. Babies of young mothers with large families for their age have a high risk of death in the post-neonatal period.

Economic conditions play an important part in determining mortality levels. Generally infant mortality is two and a half times as great in Social Class V (unskilled workers) as in Social Class I (professional and administrative workers); the gradient is more marked for post-neonatal mortality than for stillbirths and neonatal mortality. For any social class infant, mortality is higher in the North of England and in Wales than elsewhere.

Foetal mortality is higher for illegitimate births than for legitimate births, as can be seen from the following figures.

England and Wales 1955

	All infants	Illegitimate
Stillbirth rate (per 1,000 total births)	23.2	28.8
Early neonatal rate (per 1,000 related births)	14.6	20.8
Late neonatal rate (per 1,000 related births)	2.6	3.1
Post-neonatal rate (per 1,000 related births) (4 weeks and under 1 year)	7.6	7.8

It will be seen that the excess is mainly in the peri-natal period. As to the cause of this excess it has to be borne in mind that the social factors referred to above operate adversely in that section of the population in which illegitimacy tends to have a higher incidence.

But it is not only a question of social conditions. The level of living will be generally lower for those bearing illegitimate babies. No direct comparison is possible as the father is not invariably recorded at registration of illegitimate births, but of mothers of illegitimate infants born in 1951 in England and Wales 23 per cent were in occupations of Social Classes IV and V, and 49 per cent were unoccupied, while 26 per cent of legitimate births were to women married to husbands in Social Classes IV and V or unoccupied. (General Register Office, 1957, no. 48). If only a fraction of the 49 per cent unoccupied were living in conditions appropriate to Social Classes IV and V, this makes the comparison unfavourable to illegitimate babies. Nevertheless other factors are involved. We are dealing with a less responsible section of the community. The level of intelligence and standards of prenatal and maternal care tend to be lower, there is more likelihood of reluctance to seek medical care at an early stage or to cooperate with such medical care, and general standards of hygiene will be lower. The result is that even for the same social class the illegitimate births are subject to higher mortality rates.

England and Wales 1949-53

	Social Class (of mother for illegitimate and father for legitimate births)				
	I	II	III	IV	V
Stillbirth rate (per 1,000 total births)					
legitimate	16.3	19.9	22.5	24.5	27.4
illegitimate	(46.8)	31.1	32.4	35.5	37.8
Neonatal mortality (per 1,000 live births)					
legitimate	14.0	15.6	18.3	20.0	22.8
illegitimate	(13.3)	34.9	28.9	31.0	38.2

An even more informative study has been conducted in the northern regions of France (Girard, Henry and Nistri, 1959, no. 67). This showed that independently of economic level, infant mortality was higher in (1) families

47

which did not take summer holidays (2) those with poorer parental care (3) those where there was not a habitual daily bath (4) those where infants were not taken out daily (5) those with irregular weighing of babies (6) those with poor diets (7) those where the behaviour of mother and children was poor (8) those where little regard was had to the importance of sanitation.

The enquiry showed clearly that sickness and disease affected more often those families, centres and towns which offered least resistance, through lack of health education. The authors emphasised that these findings were not necessarily applicable to other towns and centres where the death rate was higher than in the Nord. "One is often surprised to find that the region where economic advance is already ahead suffers such backwardness in the matter of health. An urban area established earlier than others where buildings have not been renewed or renovated, where there is a low level of instruction, especially in regard to the teaching of obstetric matters to wives who marry very young, where there is high rate of fecundity among the working class, where housing conditions are often defective, where medical-social services are lacking and which, in any case, would not meet requirements if the status of the area was to change unexpectedly, where life has been hard for many generations – centred in the mines and the factories – where a large proportion of the population is working class, where the lower grade of employers, clerks, etc., is partly recruited from the working classes, maintaining sometimes many of their cultural habits, where, although traditional cleanliness exists, the sense of hygiene is much less developed, all these things provide a collection of factors sufficient to explain the backwardness in that area in the fight against infant mortality. It is not certain that one would find similar conditions existing elsewhere."

The enquiry formed a strong presumption in favour of the existence, alongside the lack of medical-social services, of a group of other causes which could be described as cultural and social.

There are two important features of these investigations to be noted. First the comparatively short interval between birth and death renders it possible to assume that the social, economic and cultural characteristics of the family at the birth of the infant (many of which may be readily ascertained in connection with that event) may be reliably assumed to operate up to the point of death and to be directly associated with death. In the observation of adult mortality on the other hand we have noted that antecedent conditions operate over a longer period of time during which there is much opportunity for variation so that it is much more difficult to isolate the influences relevant

48

to mortality. An adult may die in conditions very different from those operating at the commencement of the terminal illness. Retrospective assessment of the contributory factors is correspondingly hazardous and subject to error. Secondly it will be noted that the extension of the study of mortality to educational and cultural factors inevitably introduces an element of subjective judgment of the "good, fair, bad" type. This means that great care has to be taken to establish definitions of criteria that are (1) reproducible, in the sense that any set of similar assessments identifies a set of exactly similar circumstances, and (2) capable of uniform application. "Bad parental care" is a relative, not an absolute, description. Unless concepts can be clearly defined, interpretation of mortality differentials may be difficult and even misleading. Where subjective assessment cannot be avoided it is a good rule to contrast extreme groups and to evade the almost impossible interpretation of the experience of intermediate groups where homogeneity is most lacking. The "very good" are all likely to be "good", and the "very bad", "bad" but those in between may shade imperceptibly from "good" to "bad".

EDUCATION AND CULTURE

Those in professional and managerial employment have lighter mortality than unskilled workers. The former are also better educated, in health and in all matters, than the latter. Does education have an effect independently of socio-economic conditions? Is it possible to separate the two effects? General experience suggest that both questions should be answerable in the affirmative. The impact of the inimical forces of nature is clearly different for different economic levels but clearly individuals at the same economic level may react differently and take different decisions in response to external stimuli according to their cultural background. The subconscious estimation of probabilities which form the basis of their reactive decisions must depend upon education and training. Life, especially urban life, is full of dangers and, economic conditions apart, our only equipment for combatting these dangers is our native intelligence and a storehouse of experience. The more educated we are, the more codified is this experience, the quicker we assess the probable balance of advantage of this or that reaction to danger. To take an elementary example: in order to combat infectious external diseases our forefathers taught us lessons about washing hands after defaecation and before handling food. Whether these lessons have been communicated to

us, whether we appreciate them and whether we apply in specific circumstances is largely a matter of education. Education plays a part in deciding
whether we clothe ourselves or feed ourselves adequately; what we do about
fresh air, exercise, and relaxation; whether we avoid excessive indulgence in
alcoholic consumption or tobacco or other harmful habits; whether we take
holidays or not and what we do in them; whether, should disability of any
kind overcome us, we successfully adapt ourselves to it. Economic conditions soon come into the picture. They restrain our freedom of action in all
these matters. It is more difficult to be clean without hot water. The more
protective foods and those with a higher protein content are generally the
more expensive. To escape from the oppression of the town even for a short
annual holiday may not be possible for those with low incomes. On the
other hand education favours social mobility and alone offers the means of
breaking these economic restraints.

Up to the present very little progress has been made in this area of mortality study, except in relation to peri-natal mortality where the cultural
situation of the families is under observation and not that of the individuals
whose mortality is being studied; for infants have no educational background. The studies of Girard and his colleagues to which reference has
already been made, illustrate the way in which the studies of infant mortality
have been extended to bring in the cultural factor. Poor mothercraft has
long been recognised as an important factor in infant mortality and it has
been stressed as an obstacle to progress in those less developed countries
where infant mortality is still high (Chandrasekhar 1959, no. 79).

It is worth recalling the experience of England and Wales at the beginning
of this century when infant mortality was high. The factors involved, which
were emphasised by public health workers at that time, were poverty,
uncleanliness, overcrowding, alcoholic indulgence and disease, poor water
supply, unsatisfactory food storage, conservancy disposal as distinct from
water-carriage of excreta, inefficient scavenging, but most of all abandonment
of breastfeeding without adequate cause. It was known that breastfeeding
was associated with lower incidence of infectious disease, especially enteritis.

It was these factors which the public health authorities attacked. Under
the influence of French medicine (Herrgot in Nancy and Budin in Paris)
infant welfare centres gradually appeared on the scene. A beginning was
made with the establishment of a number of milk depots to provide clean
cows' milk to mothers unable to breastfeed. A school for mothers was opened
in London in 1904, and another in 1907. The generations of women then

50

passing through their childbearing life were the first to benefit from compulsory education under the Act of 1870 so that health education was receiving ready acceptance. An infant welfare centre (so called) was opened in London in 1913. By 1917 London had 100 such centres. In 1918 the Government made these centres a compulsory function of public health authorities. About the same time a personal approach to education in maternal care was intensified through health visitors who were, from 1907, notified of all births in order that they might make early contact with the mother. Health visitors established a bond of confidence between themselves and the vast majority of mothers and succeeded in conveying to mothers the simple truths of asepsis, nutrition and physical development. A third contemporary advance was a rise in the standard of midwifery following the establishment of the Central Midwives Board in 1902. As a result infant mortality plunged downward, from 156 per 1,000 live births in the period 1896-1900 to 90 for the period 1916-1920 and 55 for 1936-1940.

In South Africa, similar progress has been observed in rural communities after the foundation of community health education and an increase in the skilled medical and nursing care available. Reporting this progress Kark and Chester (1956, no. 114) have drawn a distinction between a high standard of formal education enjoyed, for example, by certain Zulu communities and their less adequate health education. Infant mortality was higher in the Zulu than in Hindu communities though the former had a higher standard of formal education and made more use of medical services. They say "the persistent belief in witchcraft which exists in our Zulu communities leads to action of a kind which not only may be harmful, but which often delays or interrupts medical care. On the other hand, our more limited experience with Hindu communities indicates that, while the family frequently turns to traditionally recognised diagnosticians and healers for the prevention and treatment of illness, these visits do not necessarily conflict with their use of modern medical services." Kark and Chester point to other factors which are probably involved – the stability of family living and family solidarity, and the way in which communities adapt themselves to adverse conditions. These considerations take us into the field of anthropology. A vitally important area of research has been opened up; for over the vast underdeveloped areas of the world, population is on the move from the country to the town and the cultural forces which are thus placed under strain may be all important to their well-being.

Even in the field of infant mortality where an approach to the study of the

51

contribution of education and culture has been made, the results are so far scanty. As to the assessment of their contribution to adult mortality a beginning has hardly been made though it must come soon.

AVAILABILITY OF MEDICAL SERVICES

A positive factor for health all over the world has been the growth, coincident with general economic development, in the provision of community medical services. The history of public health in the developed countries shows, however, that these services are of little avail against the major factor of poverty and it is only in recent decades when the grosser forms of poverty have been eliminated in the developed countries that the real effect of freely accessible medical care of a high technical standard can be observed. In such countries especially those where advanced forms of social medicine have been developed in conditions of full employment and economic security that major benefits to health have been secured. So long as these services are generally accessible it does not matter a great deal whether they are provided by schemes of social insurance or by individual contracts of private insurance. Vast campaigns of immunisation now protect communities against diseases – diphtheria, smallpox, tuberculosis – which formerly killed great numbers. Other public health services which have been with us longer must not be forgotten. Efficient sewage disposal, pure drinking water and pasteurised milk have banished the pestilences which once ravaged urban populations. Organised child welfare schemes and school health services with routine medical inspections, in conjunction with the family doctor ensure that the child and adolescent grow up under constant medical supervision with treatment facilities immediately available for any departure from normal development. For adults the accessible diagnostic services (the general practitioner and hospital outpatient department) ensure early detection of disease. Modern surgery in an era of antibiotics now reaches the most deep seated disease. Medical advances have permitted other diseases – diabetes for example – which are not amenable to surgery to be corrected where formerly they pursued a relentless course to death. A number of reductions in mortality from specific diseases can be associated with these advances in preventive and curative medicine. The elimination of poverty has been a major factor in the reduction of tuberculosis prevalence but streptomycin and other chemotherapy together with bold surgery (Benjamin and Logan, 1957, no. 118) have ensured that the disease when it

52

does occur is only infrequently fatal. The introduction of sulpha drugs has reduced mortality from pneumonia to minor proportions. Diabetics lead a normal life. A number of forms of organic heart disease are no longer regarded as necessarily foreshortening life (Society of Actuaries, 1954, no. 141). Mortality from many forms of cancer (other than lung cancer) has been considerably reduced. Surgical treatment has dramatically reduced the risk of fatal perforation and infection in appendicitis and peptic ulcer. Deaths from strangulated hernia and other anatomical disturbances in the abdomen are fewer. The treatment of injury (especially fractures) is now immensely safer. Even in chronic and degenerative diseases, for example bronchitis or myocardial degeneration, disability has been reduced and life prolonged if only fractionally.

It is difficult to place statistical values upon these contributions to reduced mortality because though modern urban life provides these preventive and curative services it also adds stresses which increase the risk of disease (and we discuss this later). The important point to be made here is that in conditions of universal accessibility of these medical services unrestrained by any economic barriers, social and economic differentials in mortality are correspondingly reduced. Where treatment is available according to need rather than according to income then the changes of recovery of the rich and poor are much less unequal; and differences between town and country are also reduced.

THE MODE OF LIVING

The striking feature of mortality trends in some developed countries has been the failure of mortality at older ages in men to improve in contrast to the steady decline in death rates for women at all ages. Two causes of mortality stand out as contributing increasing numbers of deaths which more than offset reductions in numbers of deaths from other causes – cancer of the lung and bronchus and arterial heart disease. That this is happening only in males and only in some countries suggests that some features of the way of life of men in these countries may be responsible. What these features are is still the subject of controversy but a considerable amount of circumstantial evidence is accumulating.

The evidence in relation to smoking has been well brought together by the Royal College of Physicians in the United Kingdom in a report of a special committee (1962, no. 64). The committee summarise the situation in the following way: "Several serious illnesses, in particular lung cancer, affect smokers more often than non-smokers. Heavier smokers have a higher death rate than lighter smokers: those who continue to smoke have a higher death rate than those who stop: cigarette smokers have a higher death rate than smokers of pipes or cigars. There is no doubt of the truth of these statements; dispute continues only about their interpretation."

The report examines the chemistry and pharmacology of smoking. It admits that tobacco smoke is an extremely complex mixture of 300 compounds and that little is known of the medical importance of the variations arising from type and mode of curing of tobacco and the way it is smoked. Cigarette smoke is acid and hotter than smoke from cigars or pipes. Sixteen substances which are carcinogenic to experimental animals have been isolated but exposure of animals to tobacco smoke in inhaled air has failed to produce lung cancers and the causative hypothesis has to rest on other evidence than this. In the respiratory tract tobacco smoke stimulates the secretion of mucous and delays its removal and this is likely to favour the production of bronchitis. The arsenic content of tobacco smoke is infinitesimal but may have a cocarcinogenic effect.

It has been argued that some people are genetically susceptible to lung cancer and that their smoking is merely a symptom and not a cause of this condition. This is a plausible theory and it has not been disproved but it is difficult to square this hypothesis with the time changes in mortality which make it necessary to postulate that there is some causative agent to which human lungs have been *newly* and *increasingly* exposed in the 20th century. Not only does cigarette smoke fit the bill but the tight relationship between lung cancer mortality and the amount of cigarettes smoked and the lowered risk in those who have given up smoking provides powerful supporting evidence. There are three principal pathological types of lung cancer and smoking is associated specifically with two of these.

The most obvious explanation of the association between smoking and lung cancer is the causative one, but alternative and more complicated hypotheses are considered. These are (1) the desire to smoke is a precancerous condition. However, since this process must, if true, begin 40 or 50 years before the onset of clinical disease it seems improbable (2) smoking merely determines the site of cancer in a person predisposed to the disease. But other sites are not less common in smokers than non-smokers (3) the genetic hypothesis referred to above and rejected for the reason stated and on the evidence of phenomenally low incidence of lung cancer in the Seventh

54

Day Adventists who are all non-smokers and who have no general immunity to cancer (4) that the rising death rate from cancer is a consequence of the falling death rate from tuberculosis, i.e. a reflection of the survival of the unfit respiratory systems. This does not fit the association with smoking (5) that smoking accelerates ageing and therefore advances the onset of higher risk of cancer. But why lung cancer particularly? (6) common association of lung cancer and smoking with alcohol consumption. But the association of lung cancer with smoking is independent of alcohol (7) motor vehicle exhausts. There is, however, no evidence of higher risk in road haulage workers (8) air pollution generally. This is less important than and merely additive to the smoking factor. To remove it would reduce but not eliminate lung cancer.

All in all the committee finds it difficult to avoid accepting the simplest explanation. They admit the existence of untidy ends, e.g. the evidence on inhaling is equivocal, the male/female differential in incidence of lung cancer is not fully explained (though this may be because women have only in recent times taken to heavy cigarette smoking), and the causal mechanism has not been established. They point out, however, that when cholera was found to be water-borne action was taken to purify water and to banish epidemics long before the causal organism was isolated.

Lung cancer is not the only risk. Bronchitis, tuberculosis, coronary heart disease and cancer of some sites other than lung are involved and smoking impairs the rate of healing of peptic ulcers.

The main British source of data is the prospective study of Doll and Hill (1956, no. 61) which covered the experience of 40,000 men and women medical practitioners followed up for 4 years from 1951. Smokers were graded into three groups (1-14 cigarettes a day, 15-24 a day and 25 or more a day). The third group included only a small number of lives. The mortality differential between the first two groups was trivial and it is possible to combine these two groups. The ratios of age rates of mortality for all causes to those for non-smokers are shown below. It is important to deal with all causes since differentials are involved not only for lung cancer but also for bronchitis, tuberculosis, coronary heart disease and cancer of some sites other than lung.

The table also shows mortality ratios for two American studies (1) that of Hammond and Horn (1958, no. 63), which traced 187,783 white males of ages between 50 and 69 from early 1952 to October 1955, covering 667,753 man-years of exposure, (2) that of Dorn (1959, no. 62) which covered the mortality experience of 200,000 army veterans who were policy holders of U.S. Government life insurance; it included 478,952 person-years of exposure. The ratios shown for these two studies were practically invariant with age.

Age	Ratio of cigarette smokers' mortality rate (all causes) to non-smokers		
	Doll & Hill	Hammond & Horn	Dorn
35-44	1.41		
45-54	1.72		
55-64	1.59		
65-74	1.41		
All ages		1.57	1.32

It looks therefore as if mortality rates are higher by at least one third for cigarette smokers as compared with non-smokers and that the proportionate rise is early and unlikely to vary with age. As to the importance of this factor we need only remark that in Britain more than two thirds of adult males are addicted to cigarette smoking. It has also to be borne in mind that heavy smokers are also more likely to be heavy drinkers and they are therefore likely to suffer the risks associated with high alcohol consumption (Dawber et al. 1959, no. 9).

The factors involved in mortality from cardiovascular disease are less clear. There is some evidence of dietary influence; it is considered that a diet rich in animal fat involves the ingestion of saturated fatty acids which lead to a high cholesterol level and may also inhibit fibrinolysis. In turn this leads to arterial deposits and coronary thrombosis, occlusion, ischaemia and cardiac failure. The mechanism is not firmly established but certainly the mortality from coronary heart disease is higher in those who are in the habit of consuming animal fat or who are overweight or who take little exercise. What we are concerned with most in the present context is a clear association between sedentary occupations and above average mortality from coronary heart disease. In the 1949-53 investigation in England and Wales (General Register Office, 1958, no. 53) for example, the standardised mortality ratios (to 100 for all occupied and retired males) at age 20-64 were:

Higher administrative occupations 147
Clerical workers 132
Foremen 99
Skilled manual workers 102
Semiskilled manual workers . . . 84
Unskilled manual workers 89
Farmers 62
Agricultural workers 55

Similar differentials were observed in the French investigation of 1955 (Febvay and Aubenque, 1957, no. 88).

An inverse relationship with education has been found but this is highly correlated with occupation and no independent effect has been demonstrated. A number of questions remain unanswered. Why, for example, is the mortality index for coronary disease lower for agricultural than for other manual workers? Is this longer working hours or differences in diet, or both?

The following death rates per 1,000 from arteriosclerotic and degenerative heart disease in men aged 45-64 are of interest (they are for the latest available year and are taken from the *U.N. Demographic Yearbook 1961*):

Country	*Rate*
United States	5.96
Israel	3.48
Japan	0.94
Austria	2.74
Belgium	2.29
Denmark	2.62
Finland	5.43
France	1.26
Italy	2.05
Netherlands	2.49
Sweden	2.43
England and Wales	3.74
Yugoslavia	0.85
New Zealand	
European	4.51
Maori	3.40

South Africa
    Coloured 3.77
    White 5.56
    Asiatic 4.85

There are some wide variations here. Clearly some are due to variations between countries in death certification practice but there are other differences which suggest the operation of environmental, probably dietary, factors. This is brought out especially by the differences between white and coloured populations in South Africa and New Zealand, between the United States and England and Wales on the one hand and Denmark, Sweden, and the Netherlands on the other. These differences are unlikely to be attributable to different medical approaches to the certification of causes of death.

The higher mortality of those who habitually consume substantial quantities of alcohol is well established. We have already noted the higher mortality of those whose occupations are associated with the sale of alcohol drinks. The predominant cause of death is cirrhosis of the liver. The death rate per 100,000 from this cause in men aged 45-64 varies from 22 in Canada to 40 in the United States; from 32 in Japan to 64 in Taiwan; from 8 in Norway and the Netherlands to 53 in Italy, 70 in Austria and 104 in France.

SOCIO-ECONOMIC GROUPS

We have seen that the inter-correlations between the various social, economic, and cultural factors are so strong that it is dangerous and misleading to study any one in isolation. For this reason many workers have regarded it as an economy of effort to concentrate on a single indication of the general level of living with which all other factors are associated in the same general direction. This indication is usually derived from the one objective characteristic which is most easily, most commonly and most accurately recorded, occupation. Sometimes industry, status (employer, manager, foreman, etc.) and whether or not economically active, are also incorporated in the one indicating classification.

The occupational classification used, for example, in England and Wales comprises several hundred unit groups to which one or more individual occupations are assigned depending upon the description on the census

58

schedule (General Register Office, 1960, no. 49). The following is a random section of the classification –

> Order IV – Glass and Ceramics Makers
> 030   Ceramic formers
> 031   Glass formers, finishers and decorators
> 032   Furnacemen, kilnmen, glass and ceramic
> 033   Ceramics decorators and finishers
> 034   Glass and ceramics production process workers n.e.c.

Any one unit will, of course, embrace a number of different descriptions, viz., "Glass formers, finishers and decorators" will include "Achromatic hand, Acider, Artist (glass decorating), Assembler (bifocal), Embosser, Mirror backer, Colour bander, Glass-tube bender, Lens blocker, Glass blower, Glass calibrator, Nickel carboniser (valves), Glass cutter, Optical engineer, Knobber, Malletter-on, Sticker-on (lens)" and others.

Each unit, however, will be broadly homogeneous in respect of the job performed (e.g. manual or non-manual, machine or hand, skill involved) and the conditions in which it is performed (indoor or outdoor, clean or dirty, sedentary or ambulant, heat or cold, long or short hours, seasonal pressure, etc.). For presenting differentials associated with general levels of living, however, it is more practical to group units together. The earliest attempts to do this gave rise to the "social classes" of the General Register Office:

I   Professional etc. occupations
II   Intermediate between I and III
III   Skilled Workers* [(a) Mineworkers (b) Transport Workers (c) Clerical Workers (d) Armed Forces (c) Others].
IV   Intermediate between III and IV* [(a) Agricultural Workers (b) Others].
V   Unskilled Workers* [(a) Building and Dock Labourers (b) Others].

The method here, is to attribute to each of the occupations distinguished in the classification a ranking based either on social values (for example, that of standing within the community, such as in Great Britain from the 1911 Census onward) or on a score derived from a battery of such values (as in the United States Census of 1960). This has two disadvantages:

* Special splits made for mortality investigation purposes 1950-52.

(i) There is a likelihood that the ranking will be influenced by preconceived notions of just those differentials of health or behaviour which the groupings are to be used to discover.

(ii) It is difficult to provide an economic interpretation of the interrelationships of the groups and other social characteristics because of the abstract and subjective character of the ranking.

(iii) The socio-economic homogeneity of the so-called "social classes" is limited by the fact that whole occupational units only are assigned to a group irrespective of the circumstances of individual workers coded to that unit.

Nevertheless the social classes do effect a broad division of the occupied population by economic and social circumstances which are more difficult to describe than to recognise.

To meet the objection raised against the "social classes" new socio-economic groups were introduced by the General Register Office at the 1961 Census as an alternative grouping to social classes. They represent an improvement in environmental homogeneity.

The method which was developed in France (Brichler, 1958, no. 5) and standardized in the European Working Group on Population Censuses of the Economic Commission for Europe is to derive groups automatically from a cross-tabulation of the four economic classifications normally used in the population census (1) type of activity (active or inactive and in the latter event the type of inactive group, e.g., hospital inmate, housewife, etc.) (2) occupation (3) employment status (employer, manager, etc.) (4) branch of economic activity (industry).

The individual cells of such a cross-tabulation represent groups with substantial homogeneity of social and economic characteristics and these can be grouped into broader groups to the extent of contraction in numbers of groups that may be desired. An important feature of these groups is the fact that they are not necessarily ranked in any preconceived order; it is claimed only that they are economically *different*, not that one group has higher social standing than another. Clearly in material terms the level of living is higher for one group than another so that some degree of economic ordering is inevitable.

The European Working Group on Population Census of E.C.E. has subjected this system to close study and have recommended the following combinations:

Socio-Economic Classification

A. *Economically active population*

1. Farm-employers
2. Farmers on own account without employees
3. Members of agricultural producers' co-operatives
4. Agricultural workers
5. Employers in industry and commerce; large enterprises
6. Employers in industry and commerce; small enterprises
7. Employers in industry and commerce; own account workers without employees
8. Liberal and related professions
9. Members of non-agricultural producers' co-operatives
10. Directors (managers) of enterprises and companies
11. Senior non-manual workers
12. Intermediate and junior non-manual workers and sales workers
13. Supervisors and skilled, semi-skilled and specialised manual workers
14. Labourers
15. Service staff (domestic servants, cleaners, caretakers) and related workers
16. Members of armed forces on compulsory military service
17. Economically active persons not classifiable in the above groups

B. *Economically inactive population*

18. Former farmer-employers
19. Former non-agricultural employers
20. Former employees
21. Other independent inactive persons
22. Children below minimum school leaving age
23. Students and school-children above minimum school leaving age
24. Housewives
25. Other adults in the home
26. Inmates of institutions.

(Further subdivisions were suggested and also summary groups, but these have been omitted in the interests of brevity).

These socio-economic groups may then be used to classify the whole population (attributing to dependents the groups of those on whom they are dependent) or the active population only, or whole households (by the group of the chief economic supporter).

The socio-economic groups introduced by the General Register Office for the 1961 Census adhered closely to the E.C.E. model, with only minor variations to adapt it to British conditions (there are no non-agricultural producers' co-operatives).

If deaths can be similarly classified by social class or socio-economic groups the mortality differentials can be examined. If this can be done within the national vital registration system the statistical investigation can be carried out on a large scale. It must be admitted immediately that this is more difficult for socio-economic groups which require for their identification more characteristics than are normally recorded at the registration of deaths; it is, for example, easier to obtain, from the informants, particulars of the deceased's occupation than of his branch of economic activity. But if this form of analysis cannot be applied to a combination of census data (populations) and vital registration records (deaths) it can be applied in ad hoc studies.

At the 1949-53 investigation (General Register Office, 1958, no. 53), the following gradients were discernible:

England and Wales
Standardised Mortality Ratios 1949-53

Ages 20-64	Social Class				
	I	II	III	IV	V
Occupied males	98	86	101	94	118
single women	82	73	89	89	92
wives of males in specified social class	96	88	101	104	110

These social class gradients differed both in steepness and in direction for different causes of death. Causes for which mortality rose steeply with social class (i.e. with *less* favourable economic circumstances) included –

62

	S.M.R.'s (males 20-64)				
	I	II	III	IV	V
Respiratory tuberculosis	58	63	102	95	143
Bronchitis	34	53	98	101	171
Pneumonia	53	64	92	105	150
Other myocardial degeneration	68	82	94	101	135
Ulcer of stomach	53	71	98	104	144
Malignant neoplasm, stomach	57	70	101	112	130

while the following causes, for example, were apparently associated with comparative affluence –

	S.M.R.'s (males 20-64)				
	I	II	III	IV	V
Acute poliomyelitis	295	171	90	63	42
Leukaemia	123	98	104	93	89
Coronary disease, angina	147	110	105	79	89
Cirrhosis of liver	207	152	84	70	96
Diabetes	134	100	99	85	105
Vascular lesions of nervous system	124	104	101	88	101
Suicide	140	113	89	92	117

and for some causes there was very little gradient at all, as for example,

Nephritis and nephrosis   102   98   100   94   105

For the socio-economic groups there are as yet no British data, but the following figures are available from French experience (Febvay and Aubenque, 1957, no. 88):

Death rates per 10,000 males aged 25-54 in 1955

4 Intermediate personnel 31
3 Liberal professions and senior personnel . . . 32
  30 Liberal professions 35
0 Farmers 42
2 Employers in industry and commerce 51
  21,22 Industrials and artisans. 43

25-27 Merchants 59

23,66 Fishermen, sailors (employers, employees) 82

5 Non-manual workers 52

1 Agricultural workers 54

6 Manual workers 56

65 Miners 66

68 Unskilled workers 76

These figures are illustrative only. Much more detailed figures are available in the French analyses.

From all that has been previously discussed in this report about the difficulties of definition of social factors and the near impossibility of separating the individual contributions to mortality of these factors (because of their intercorrelation) it does appear likely that the attempt to take mortality analysis to a greater stage of refinement than these socio-economic groups may bring only marginal improvement to set against a very great increase in labour. It is clear that given a sufficient degree of homogeneity these groups provide a powerful tool for the study of social differentials in mortality. Of course it is necessary to be sure of the social, economic and cultural characteristics of these groups and quite serious studies are involved of all those factors enumerated earlier in this report and of their variation among the groups. These studies can be carried on independently of the mortality analysis. Brichler, in his paper quoted above, has given examples of a wide range of factors which in France have been differentiated among the socio-economic groups – alcohol consumption, sickness absence, school leaving age, radio and television habits, possession of household equipment (refrigerators, washing machines, etc.), expenditure and savings, housing conditions, size of family, religious belief, etc. It would seem for be as satisfying and as simple as any approach so far devised for the exploitation of mortality data normally derived from census and vital registration records as well as those derived in ad hoc retrospective studies.

PROSPECTIVE STUDIES

Retrospective studies have not been without their major successes and there is often no alternative to the retrospective approach, but this is not the ideal research method. The scientific method which forms the basis of productive research requires that hypotheses, (in the present context about relationships between various social factors and mortality) should be constructed and validated or invalidated by experimental evidence. The information requirements of such experimentation are unlikely to be exactly fulfilled by what has already been recorded in respect of deaths which have occurred in the past and before the hypotheses could influence the system of recording. Moreover once deaths have occurred and have been recorded it is difficult to add to the record by any supplemental enquiry. The evidence grows cold very quickly; it may never have existed.

For these reasons the superiority of the prospective or longitudinal enquiry, that is the following through of a group of lives suitably selected to meet experimental requirements (if only to be representative of the general population) and observed over the course of time during which their deaths and the essential evidence specifically related to the testing of hypothesis may be recorded, is clear.

Two of many examples may be quoted. First, the Framingham Study (Dawber et al, 1959, no. 9). At this town in Massachusetts, U.S.A., the U.S. National Heart Institute has been conducting a prospective study of factors related to the development of cardiovascular disease. A random sample of two thirds of the adult population aged 29-62 years was selected for observation. The subjects, all initially free of any cardiovascular system, have been brought in for regular clinical examination. Already much useful information has been gathered about the role of hypercholesterolaemia and hypertension and many other factors are under study, for example, geographical distribution, educational status, smoking and drinking habits. Here the actual development of disease in subjects initially free of disease is under observation in individual environments which are carefully charted. Another example is that of Doll and Hill (1956, no. 61) who have followed up a representative group of medical practitioners in order to relate their smoking habits to mortality from cancer of the lung and other diseases. This represents a classical example of the prospective study both in respect of the careful statistical organisation applied and the thoroughness with which possible sources of bias were eliminated in the final analyses.

There is another important reason why the longitudinal study represents the more profitable development for future research. This takes us back to the commencement of this report where we stressed the difficulty of extending evidence of *association* between social factors and mortality to hypotheses about *causation* and where we drew attention to the long chain of events leading to death. Longitudinal studies provide the opportunity of

65

observing the emergence of the first symptoms of disease in those initially free of disease. The point of observation is therefore much farther back than the terminal condition of death and much closer to the actual conditions associated with the onset of disease. Moreover not only can there be measurements of the survival prospects for those chronic diseases with which we are now most concerned (cancer, coronary heart disease, etc.) but there can also be evaluation of the *quality* of survival (e.g. capacity for work). It must not be forgotten that an important aspect of the relationship between social and economic conditions and mortality is the way in which adaptation to disease involves in itself changes in these conditions.

Résumé français:
Facteurs sociaux et économiques de la mortalité

Introduction

La mort est le résultat final d'une chaîne d'évènements dont la durée est très variable. Il est difficile d'en déterminer l'origine précise et de distinguer des phénomènes génétiques ce qui est influence du milieu. Certaines causes de mort sont évidentes (blessure, infection), mais d'autres, qui altèrent le processus de vieillissement, le sont moins. La longévité, déterminée par des facteurs génétiques, l'est aussi par l'alimentation, etc.

Il n'a pas semblé utile dans le cadre de cette étude de distinguer le vieillissement des maladies cliniquement identifiables. En revanche les relations empiriques entre la mortalité et les facteurs économiques et sociaux mesurables sont envisagées, étant entendu qu'il faudrait parfois remonter aux facteurs génétiques.

Le passage de la relation "changements économiques et sociaux – changement de la mortalité" à une explication causale poserait des problèmes trop complexes. Nous ne formulons donc pas d'hypothèses précises dans ce sens, mais nous nous contentons d'observer en action (par le moyen des statistiques) les facteurs de la mortalité.

Définition des facteurs sociaux et économiques

L'objet de cette étude est constitué par un large éventail d'éléments déterminant l'interaction de l'homme et des conditions extérieures: confrontation avec les phénomènes naturels, lutte pour la vie dans le domaine économique, position sociale, intégration au groupe, réaction aux mœurs. La réussite ou l'échec du processus global d'adaptation aux contraintes extérieures reflète la santé ou la maladie. Ce processus est le mécanisme superficiel de variation de la mortalité. De nombreux éléments de l'environnement l'influencent: conditions de travail, éducation, niveau de vie (alimentation, logement loisirs, etc.). A cela s'ajoutent l'arrière plan culturel, la religion, les coutumes, etc. (Benjamin, 1955, no. 68).

La relation entre les facteurs ainsi isolés et les conditions économiques semble parfois lointaine, mais n'en est pas moins réelle. Une pollution atmosphérique sera plus fortement ressentie par ceux dont les conditions de vie économique sont telles qu'il ne peuvent changer de domicile ou de profession. Par ailleurs, les traditions peuvent survivre au changement économique; la mobilité sociale est lente; elle n'est pas inévitable.

Mesure des facteurs sociaux et économiques
Si l'on ne peut qu'observer superficiellement la cause des décès, l'observation des changements du milieu social, économique et culturel est, elle aussi, difficile. Tous les éléments de l'environnement se prêtent mal à la quantification au sein des groupes où l'on observe la mortalité. Au niveau de l'individu on peut mesurer l'alimentation, les conditions de logement, l'urbanisation, la pratique religieuse, les habitudes d'hygiène, etc. S'agissant du groupe, ces mêmes éléments ne sont pas toujours susceptibles de mesure. Il est souvent impossible d'obtenir des mesures spécifiques pour des groupes définis. L'expérimentation n'est pas possible avec les hommes: on ne peut tester l'influence du milieu. Il faut donc découvrir des portions de groupes, naturelles et homogènes, soumises à un facteur spécifique. Cela pose dans la réalité de nombreux problèmes (cf. Benjamin, 1963, sur la tuberculose, no. 2).

L'analyse factorielle peut être un efficace moyen de classification. Buckatzsch (1947, no. 7), Moser, et Scott (1961, no. 13) l'ont utilisée pour étudier la typologie urbaine en Grande Bretagne, définissant 57 variables pour réduire en groupes cohérents une mosaïque de complexes urbains. Cette analyse comporte des limites.

Le niveau de vie
Bien que cette notion soit d'une importance croissante, elle se prête mal à l'analyse. Le problème s'est posé, en particulier dans le cadre de l'aide aux pays sous-développés, afin de définir les priorités et de mesurer les résultats (Rapport du comité des experts de l'O.N.U., 1954, no. 16; étude de Moser, 1957, sur la Jamaïque, no. 12). Si chaque chercheur sait ce qu'il entend par "niveau de vie", aucun n'est à même de le réduire à un certain nombre d'éléments mesurables, valables pour tous les pays et par là même comparables. Le rapport de l'O.N.U. retenait 12 éléments (santé, nourriture, loge-

ment, etc.). Moser regroupe les indicateurs en trois grandes catégories (ressources, utilisation des ressources, résultats finaux). Il propose de normaliser chaque niveau de vie national selon des schémas propres, car on ne peut valablement comparer des pays radicalement différents (par leurs climats, leurs lois, etc.). Ces schémas, fondés sur les "besoins", utiliseront des critères semblables. Le travail reste à faire et cette méthode n'a pas encore été strictement appliquée aux différences en matière de mortalité.

Changements dans le temps des taux de mortalité

Une méthode possible (bien que quelque peu grossière) d'analyse des facteurs sociaux et économiques est d'établir une corrélation entre la mortalité et les changements historiques de la situation sociale ou des activités des services de santé publique (McKeown et Brown étudiant les changements de la mortalité au 18ème siècle en Angleterre et au Pays de Galles, no. 153; McKeown et Record recherchant les raisons du déclin de la mortalité pendant le 19ème siècle pour ces mêmes pays no. 154). Les auteurs concluent que la chute de la mortalité est moins due aux progrès médicaux qu'aux améliorations du milieu. George Stolnitz (1955 et 1956, no. 157) a examiné les tendances internationales de la mortalité au 19ème siècle et s'est efforcé de résumer les principales généralisations que l'on peut en dégager.

Les études par génération sont un autre moyen utilisé pour isoler les effets des changements sociaux sur la mortalité (Derrick, 1927, no. 152; Davidson et Reid, 1929, no. 149; Springett, 1950, no. 156, etc.). Il faut alors tenir compte du fait qu'un développement génétique peut affecter des générations successives, de même qu'un changement social peut être vécu par plusieurs générations à des âges différents.

L'alimentation

De grands progrès ont été faits dans la connaissance des conséquences qu'entrainent les excès ou les carences alimentaires. On doit distinguer entre les situations résultant d'une insuffisance du développement économique (ou de la guerre, ou d'une catastrophe...), et celles où, les fournitures alimentaires étant quantitativement et qualitativement suffisantes, des maladies d'origine alimentaire apparaissent par suite de la pauvreté ou de l'ignorance.

Le principal facteur de mortalité à prendre en considération est le manque de nourriture dans de vastes zones sous-développées. Sukhatme (1961, no. 42), se fondant sur une échelle internationale des besoins en calories, aboutit à la conclusion que 300 à 500 millions d'individus sont sous-alimentés. Un tiers ou la moitié de l'humanité souffre de la faim ou d'une mauvaise alimentation. Il faudrait d'ici 1980 doubler les approvisoinnements.

La relation mortalité-sous-alimentation est compliquée par le fait qu'il existe des causes spécifiques de mortalité, dans les pays tropicaux par exemple (malaria); mais la comparaison entre calories consommées et nombre de décès n'en est pas moins éloquente. Le progrès médical a réduit les pires effets des déficiences qualitatives (beri-beri, scorbut), mais il ne peut combattre la sous-alimentation.

Dans le cadre de cette étude il faut envisager des aspects plus spécifiques de l'alimentation. De nombreuses maladies sont liées à la carence en vitamines (le rachitisme, souvent dû au manque de la vitamine D qui permet l'absortion du calcium, le scorbut, le béri-béri, etc.). Ces maladies, plus répandues là où dominent la pauvreté et l'ignorance, ont pratiquement été extirpées de la plupart des pays développés où les statistiques permettraient leur étude. Il est très difficile de déterminer exactement le rôle de ces carences alimentaires qui sont le plus souvent liées à d'autres conditions sociales défavorables.

Il est plus facile d'étudier la liaison entre suralimentation, obésité et mortalité: les conséquences physiologiques de l'obésité (maladies cardiovasculaires, etc.) sont connues; cependant, le rôle des facteurs économiques et sociaux n'est pas univoque: l'obésité peut être liée à la pauvreté et provoquée par la substitution d'hydrates de carbones bon marché aux protéines coûteuses, etc.

La profession

On sait que la façon de gagner sa vie et le lieu du travail ont une influence importante sur la santé. Là encore, il est difficile de discerner l'influence des facteurs directement liés à la profession, en la distinguant des éléments plus généraux du niveau de vie. On doit utiliser ici les informations fournies par les recensements et les tables de mortalité. Toute étude comparative de la mortalité professionnelle doit commencer par une normalisation des âges. Un taux brut conduirait à comparer des populations différentes.

Les enquêtes du "Registrar general of England and Wales" envisagent séparément hommes, femmes mariées, femmes célibataires. Les femmes mariées sont classées selon l'emploi de leur mari, ce qui permet de dégager l'influence réelle de la profession. Si elles subissent la même mortalité excessive que leurs conjoints celle-ci est due au milieu dans son ensemble et non pas à la profession. Deux systèmes de normalisation par âge ont été utilisés.

Mais il est encore plus difficile d'interpréter les données que de calculer les indices. Recensements et tables de mortalité ne coïncident pas toujours. Les déclarations peuvent être inexactes: l'individu peut surévaluer son statut; la famille peut agir de même. En général, le recensement fournit des renseignements plus précis. Ces différences ont été examinées à l'occasion du recensement de 1951 pour l'Angleterre et le Pays de Galles.

Une difficulté supplémentaire résulte de ce que le décès est normalement mis en rapport avec le dernier emploi. Or, il peut y avoir une auto-sélection quand un individu choisit un emploi déterminé en raison de son état de santé. Des occupations légères sont exercées parce que le sujet est malade ou fatigué (vendeurs de journaux, fabricants de paniers, etc.). Un taux de mortalité élevé n'aura pas alors de signification rigoureuse.

Il est finalement très difficile de discerner si une mortalité excessive est due au risque professionnel ou au milieu en général.

On dispose donc ici d'un instrument grossier, qui peut cependant permettre de dégager des différences méritant d'être étudiées par des moyens plus précis.

L'enquête de 1949-1953 sur l'Angleterre et le Pays de Galles (no. 53) fournit un exemple des résultats obtenus et des différences de mortalité dues à des causes professionnelles.

L'urbanisation

Le phénomène urbain a été dans le passé associé à des facteurs défavorables (taudis, fumée, absence de services de santé, etc.). La situation s'est améliorée, mais des différences subsistent. (Décès en Angleterre et au Pays de Galles en 1960: 12,4‰ dans les villes de plus de 100.000 habitants; 11‰ dans les districts ruraux).

Quelle relation existe entre la mortalité et la densité de population? La première n'est pas seulement due à la promiscuité, mais aussi à tout l'ensemble économique et social qui s'associe.

Une fois de plus, il est malaisé d'isoler un facteur. Ceux qui peuvent payer un loyer élevé sont aussi ceux qui peuvent bien se nourrir, se vêtir, etc.

Le logement

Les conditions du logement affectent la santé (le surpeuplement favorise la contagion, etc.). On s'est efforcé d'en établir une classification (Stewart, 1952, no. 35; Liverpool Housing Index, cf. no. 28, etc.).

Une difficulté immédiate se présente: on peut utiliser une classification lors d'un recensement, mais non pas lors de la déclaration d'un décès.

De plus, on retrouve toujours le même problème: comment isoler ce facteur spécifique, alors qu'il est toujours étroitement lié à son contexte...?

Le seul effet direct que l'on ait pu vraiment rattacher à de mauvaises conditions d'habitat (distingué du niveau de vie dans son ensemble) a été identifié dans le cas de maladies infectieuses, et plus particulièrement de la tuberculose.

Le mariage
Il constitue par lui-même une sélection, et il a des conséquences psycho-physiologiques favorables. Il est pratiquement impossible de séparer l'un de l'autre ces deux facteurs, dont la conséquence est la mortalité moindre des gens mariés.

Climat et géographie
Il est difficile d'isoler les conséquences du climat. Il favorise certaines maladies (malaria, fièvre jaune) mais la tuberculose des zones tropicales tient à des facteurs sociaux. Il faudrait utiliser l'analyse factorielle pour dégager l'influence spécifique des différents éléments.

Mortalité foetale et en bas-age
Elle varie beaucoup avec les classes sociales, la localisation et l'âge de la mère. Elle est plus forte chez les enfants naturels, ce qui doit être attribué à des causes sociales et culturelles (voir l'étude de 1949-1953 pour l'Angleterre et le Pays de Galles, no. 53, et celle de Girard, Henry et Nistri en 1959 pour le Nord de la France, no. 67).

L'éducation et la culture
Les travailleurs qualifiés et les cadres ont une mortalité moindre que les travailleurs non spécialisés. Ils sont aussi mieux éduqués, notamment dans le domaine sanitaire. Cette éducation a-t-elle un effet indépendamment des conditions socio-économiques? Peut-on faire la distinction? La réponse à ces deux questions doit être affirmative. S'il est certain que l'impact des facteurs défavorables varie avec les catégories sociales, il est vrai aussi que des individus du même groupe peuvent réagir de manière différente. Réactions et contre-mesures sont plus rationnelles chez celui qui est plus conscient. On enseigne ou non à un individu à se laver les mains, à faire du sport... Les conditions économiques interviennent alors: il est plus facile

d'être propre quand on dispose d'eau chaude... Une campagne systématique d'hygiène donna des résultats probants en Angleterre, au début du siècle. Il en fut de même en Afrique du Sud où la mortalité infantile était supérieure dans les communautés zoulous à standing cependant plus élevé que celui des communautés indiennes (étude de Kark et Chester, 1956, no. 114).

Les services médicaux

Le développement des services médicaux collectifs est un facteur positif mais ne devient vraiment utile que lorsque la pauvreté est vaincue. Dans des conditions d'accès généralisé à ces services, sans restrictions économiques, les différences sociales sont réduites. Si les besoins prévalent sur le revenu, elles diminuent entre riches et pauvres, villes et campagnes.

Le mode de vie

La plus forte mortalité masculine dans les pays développés (cancer et maladies cardiaques) a incité à en rechercher les causes dans le mode de vie des hommes. Ces questions sont très controversées.

Les effets du tabac sont discutés. Les fumeurs ont une plus forte mortalité, mais on a avancé que le fait de fumer pouvait être un symptome d'une prédisposition au cancer et non sa cause. Ceci n'explique pas cependant le développement du cancer du poumon au 20ème siècle (cf. les études de Doll et Hill, 1956, no. 61; de Hammond et Horn, 1958, no. 63, etc.)

Les maladies cardio-vasculaires posent des problèmes encore plus complexes. Il est certain cependant qu'un régime riche en graisses animales augmente la mortalité, de même que l'obésité ou le manque d'exercice. De nombreuses questions demeurent sans réponse.

Les conséquences de l'alcoolisme sont bien établies et ses effets sur la mortalité sont connus.

Groupes socio-économiques

Devant les inconvénients de l'analyse conduite facteur par facteur, de nombreux chercheurs ont estimé plus fécond de s'en tenir au niveau de vie en général, dans lequel tous les autres éléments sont associés dans un même ensemble. C'est ainsi qu'est opérée la classification des professions par le General Register Office en 1960 (no. 49).

Des objections ayant été avancées contre une classification fondée sur la notion de classes sociales, on s'est efforcé de remplacer celles-ci par de nouveaux groupes socio-économiques. Ils marquent un progrès dans le sens de l'homogénéïté (Brichler, 1958, no. 5; voir aussi les études de l'European working group on population census of the Economic Commission for Europe). Ces groupes, aux caractéristiques économiques et sociales homogènes, peuvent être regroupés en ensembles plus ou moins larges. Une de leurs caractéristiques importantes est de ne pas être rangés dans un ordre préconçu. On les définit uniquement par le fait qu'ils sont économiquement *différents*; aucun n'est posé comme jouissant d'un standing supérieur.

Si les décès peuvent être classés selon le même procédé on analysera les différences de mortalité. Mais il est difficile d'obtenir des renseignements complets de la part des informateurs.

La difficulté de distinguer les rôles respectifs des différents facteurs socio-économiques peut amener à conclure qu'un raffinement supplémentaire de l'analyse impliquerait un effort trop grand pour une amélioration minime. Si ces groupes sont suffisamment homogènes, ils constituent un puissant outil d'investigation.

Etudes prospectives
La méthode scientifique suppose l'élaboration d'hypothèses vérifiables expérimentalement. Elle impose la nécessité d'observations prolongées et d'études prospectives sur des groupes témoins convenablement sélectionnés (Framingham Study par Dawber et al., 1959, no. 9; Doll et Hill, 1956, no. 61). Les sujets soumis à des examens réguliers permettent la vérification des hypothèses.

C'est dans cette perspective que résident les développements les plus prometteurs des recherches futures. On a noté dans l'introduction la difficulté de la transition entre la liaison "facteurs sociaux-mortalité" et la formulation d'hypothèses quant aux causes. Les études sur des groupes témoins permettent de déceler l'apparition des premiers symptomes d'une maladie chez des individus sains. On commence l'observation bien avant la conclusion (le décès) et on suit de près les conditions réelles associées au début de la maladie. On peut ainsi procéder à des analyses qualitatives. Or, il est important de savoir comment l'adaptation à la maladie modifie les conditions sociales et économiques de la mortalité.

Bibliography

A. Methods

1. BENJAMIN, B. "The measurement of morbidity". *Journal of the Institute of actuaries* 83, 1957: 225-269.
2. BENJAMIN, B. "Tuberculosis and social conditions in the metropolitan boroughs of London". *British journal of tuberculosis* 47, 1953: 4-17.
3. BOURGEOIS-PICHAT, J. "De la mesure de la mortalité infantile". *Population* 1(1), mars 1946: 53-68.
4. BOURGEOIS-PICHAT, J. "Essai sur la mortalité 'biologique' de l'homme". *Population* 7(3), juil.-sept. 1952: 381-394.
5. BRICHLER, M. "Classification of the population by social and economic characteristics. The French experience and international recommendation". *Journal of the Royal statistical society*, Series A, 121(2), 1958: 161-189.
6. BROWNLEE, J. "Interpretation of the death statistics of infancy and childhood in relation to development and environment". *British medical journal* 3217, Aug. 26, 1922: 342-347.
7. BUCKATZSCH, E. J. "An index of social conditions in 81 County Boroughs". *Bulletin of the Oxford University institute of statistics* 8(12), 1946: 365-374.
8. BUCKATZSCH, E. J. "The influence of social conditions on mortality rates". *Population studies* 1(3), 1947: 229-248.
9. DAWBER, T. R., et al. "Some factors associated with the development of coronary heart disease". *American journal of public health* 49(10), 1959: 1349-1356.
10. DORN, H. F. "Mortality", pp. 437-471 in: Hauser, P. M., and Duncan, O. D., Eds. *The study of population: an inventory and appraisal.* Chicago, the University of Chicago press, 1959.
11. GREENWOOD, Major. "Laws of mortality from the biological point of view". *Journal of hygiene* 28, 1928: 267-294.
12. MOSER, C. A. *The measurement of levels of living with special reference to Jamaica.* London, H.M.S.O., 1957, 106 p.
13. MOSER, C. A.; SCOTT, W. *British towns.* A statistical study of their social

and economic differences. Edinburgh, London, Oliver and Boyd, 1961, 169 p.

14. PEARSON, K.; TOCHER, J. F. "On criteria for the existence of differential deathrates". *Biometrika* 11, 1915-17: 159-184.

15. *Registrar general's statistical review of England and Wales for the year 1950.* Text volume. London, H.M.S.O., 1954, 225 p.

16. UNITED NATIONS. *Report on international definition and measurement of standards and levels of living.* New York, United Nations, 1954, 98 p.

B. *Ageing Processes*

17. ANDREW, W. *Cellular changes with age.* Springfield, Ill., Charles C. Thomas, 1952, 74 p.

18. COMFORT, A. *The biology of senescence.* New York, Rinehart, 1956, 257 p.

19. MOORE, J. E.; MERRITT, H. H.; MASSELINK, R. J., Eds. *The neurologic and psychiatric aspects of the disorders of aging.* Proceedings of the Association for research in nervous and mental diseases. Baltimore, the Williams and Wilkins Co., 1956, 307 p. tabl. (Research publications of the Association for research in nervous and mental diseases. 35.)

20. SHOCK, N. W. "Age changes in some physiologic processes". *Geriatrics* 12(1), 1957: 40-48.

C. *Climate*

21. "General mortality", pp. 19-24 in: *The Registrar general's statistical review of England and Wales for the year 1950. Text, medical.* London, H.M.S.O., 1954, 226 p.

22. *Registrar general's statistical review of England and Wales for the year 1952. Text volume.* London, H.M.S.O., 1955, 256 p.

D. *Urbanisation*

23. BALLOD, C. "Die Sterblichkeit der Grosstäde" (Mortality in large towns). *Bulletin de l'Institut international de statistique* (Berlin) 14(2), 1904: 401-416.

24. CASTILLO PLAZA, A. "In the light of the agrarian reform: morbidity in the rural area and comments on mortality in Venezuela". *Revista venezolana de sanidad y asistencia social* 25, Dec. 60: 141-150. [In Spanish. Quoted from *Population Index*.]

25. FARR, W. *Fifth annual report of the Registrar general of England and Wales.* London, H.M.S.O., 1843, 603 p.

26. NEWSHOLME, A. "The vital statistics of Peabody Buildings and other artisans and labourers' block dwellings". *Journal of the Royal statistical society* 54(1), Mar. 1891: 70-111.

27. STOCKS, P. "Cancer and bronchitis mortality in relation to atmospheric deposit and smoke". *British medical journal* 5114, Jan. 10, 1959: 74-79.

E. Housing

28. BARBER, R.; BLASCHKO, M. "Oxford child health survey. An assessment of housing conditions based on the Liverpool Housing Index". *The Medical officer* 91, 1954: 5-8.

29. CHALKE, H. D. "Modern methods for the control of tuberculosis". *The Medical officer* 89, 1953: 183-189.

30. HEWITT, D.; STEWART, A. "Some epidemiological aspects of acute rheumatism". *British journal of social medicine* 6(3), July 1952: 161-168.

31. KELLGREN, J. H.; LAWRENCE, J. S.; AITKEN-SWAN, J. "Rheumatic complaints in an urban population". *Annals of the rheumatic diseases (London)* 12(1), 1953: 5-15.

32. SCOTT, J. A. "Gastro-enteritis in infancy". *British journal of preventive and social medicine* 7(4), October 1953: 194-204.

33. SMITH, C. M. *Housing conditions and respiratory diseases: Morbidity in a poor-class quarter and in a rehousing area in Glasgow.* London, H.M.S.O., 1934, 36 p. (Medical research council. Special report series. 192).

34. STEIN, L. "Tuberculosis and the 'social complex' in Glasgow". *British journal of social medicine* 6(1), Jan. 1952: 1-48.

35. STEWART, A. M.; RUSSELL, W. T. "Interim report on Oxford child health survey". *The Medical officer* 88, 1952: 5-9.

36. STOCKS, P. "The association between mortality and density of housing". *Proceedings of the Royal society of medicine* (2), 1934: 1127-1146.

F. Nutrition

37. DUBLIN, L. I.; MARKS, H. H. *Mortality among insured overweights in recent years.* Sixtieth annual meeting of the Association of life insurance medical directors of America. New York, 1951, 31 p.

38. MCFIE, J. "Malnutrition in Uganda. Examination of an official statement". *Lancet* (1), 1959: 91-94.

39. MURRAY, M. B. *The effect of maternal social conditions and nutrition upon birth-weight and birth-length.* London, H.M.S.O., 1924, 34 p. (Medical research council. Special report series. 81.)

40. PAULING, L. "The relation between longevity and obesity in human beings". *Proceedings of the National academy of sciences of the U.S.A.* 44(6), 1958: 619-622.

41. ROCKSTEIN, M. *The biology of ageing in insects.* The lifespan of animals, ed. by Wolstenholme G. E. W. and O'Connor Maeve. Ciba Foundation Colloquia on Ageing. London, J. and A. Churchill, 1959, 2 vol., 32 et 26 p.

42. SUKHATME, P. V. "The world's hunger and future needs in food supplies". *Journal of the Royal statistical society*, Series A, 124(4), 1961: 463-525.

43. WIDDOWSON, E. M. *A study of individual children's diets.* London, H.M.S.O., 1947, 196 p. (Medical research council. Special report series. 257.)

G. Occupation

44. BRINTON, H. P.; FRASIER, E. S.; KOVAN, A. L. "Morbidity and mortality experience among chromate workers – respiratory cancer and other causes". *Public health reports* 67(9), 1952: 835-847.

45. CASE, R. A. M.; HOSKER, M. E. "Tumour of the urinary bladder as an occupational disease in the rubber industry in England and Wales". *British journal of preventive and social medicine* 8(2), April 1954: 39-50.

46. CASE, R. A. M.; HOSKER, M. E.; McDONALD, D. B.; PEARSON, J. T. "Tumours of the urinary bladder in workmen engaged in the manufacture and use of certain dyestuff intermediates in the British chemical industry". *British journal of industrial medicine* 11, 1954: 75-104.

47. CLEMMESEN, J. "On the etiology of some human cancers". *Journal of the National cancer institute* 12(1), 1951: 1-21.

48. GENERAL REGISTER OFFICE. *Census 1951, England and Wales, General report*. London, H.M.S.O., 1958, 224 p.

49. GENERAL REGISTER OFFICE. *Classification of occupations*. London, H.M.S.O., 1960, 136 p.

50. HAUSER, P. M.; KITAGAWA, E. M. "Social and economic mortality differentials in the U.S.A. 1960: outline of a research project", pp. 116-120 in: *Proceedings of the social statistics section*. Washington, D.C., American statistical association, 1960.

51. LEDERMANN, S. "Estimation de l'espérance de vie à la naissance par catégorie professionnelle en France". *Population* 15(1), janv.-mars 1960: 127-131.

52. PERRY, K. M. A. "Diseases of lung resulting from occupational dusts other than silica". *Thorax* 2, 1947: 91-120.

53. *Registrar general's decennial supplement, England and Wales, 1951. Part II, Occupational mortality*. London, H.M.S.O., 1958, 171 p.

54. STOCKWELL, E. G. "Socioeconomic status and mortality in the United States". *Public health reports* 76(12), 1961: 1081-1086.

H. Marriage

55. CIOCCO, A. "On the mortality in husbands and wives". *Human biology* 12(4), 1940: 508-529.

56. KRAUS, A. S.; LILIENFIELD, A. M. "Some epidemiological aspects of the high mortality rate in the young widowed group". *Journal of chronic diseases* 10(3), 1959: 207-217.

57. "Mortality according to marital status", pp. 164-171 in: *The Registrar general's statistical review of England and Wales for the year 1959. Part III. Commentary*. London, H.M.S.O., 1961, 259 p.

58. SHEPS, M. C. "Marriage and mortality". *American journal of public health* 51(4), 1961: 547-555.

59. "Sterblichkeit (Die) nach dem Familien Stand" (Mortality by marital condition). *Wirtschaft und Statistik* 12(9), Sept. 1960: 533-534.

I. *Smoking*

60. CROSS, K. W.; MCDOWELL, L. A.; POSNER, E. "Current smoking habits in 1957". *British medical journal* 5075, April 12, 1958: 862-865.

61. DOLL, R.; HILL, A. B. "Lung cancer and other causes of death in relation to smoking. A second report on the mortality of British doctors". *British medical journal* 5.001, Nov. 10, 1956: 1071-1081.

62. DORN, H. F. "Tobacco consumption and mortality from cancer and other diseases". *Public health reports* 74(7), 1959: 581-593.

63. HAMMOND, E. C.; HORN, D. "Smoking and death rates. Report on forty-four months of follow-up of 187, 783 men". *Journal of the American medical association* 166(10), 1958: 1159-1172.

64. ROYAL COLLEGE OF PHYSICIANS OF LONDON. *Smoking and health.* London, Pitman medical publishing Co, 1962, 70 p.

J. *Education and Culture*

65. BIRABEN, J. N. "Les facteurs sociaux et culturels de la mortalité infantile". *Le Concours médical* 83(19), 1961: 2801-2809.

66. GIRARD, A. "Mortalité infantile et milieu social: une enquête sur le comportement familial", pp. 396-401 in: *International Population Conference,* Vienne, 1959.

67. GIRARD, A.; HENRY, L.; NISTRI, R. *Facteurs sociaux et culturels de la mortalité infantile.* Une enquête sur le comportement des familles dans le Nord et le Pas-de-Calais. Paris, Presses universitaires de France, 1960, 211 p. (Institut national d'études démographiques. Travaux et documents. Cahier 36.)

68. PAUL, B. D.; MILLER, W. B., Eds. *Health, culture and community.* New York, Russell Sage Foundation, 1955, 493 p.

69. UPCHURCH, H. M. "A tentative approach to the study of mortality differentials between educational strata in the United States". *Rural sociology* 27(2), June 1962: 213-217.

K. *Other Environmental*

70. ALEATI, G. *La popolazione di Pavia durante il dominio spagnolo.* Milano, A. Giuffre, 1957, VIII-290 p.

71. ANDERSON, O. W. "Age-specific mortality in selected Western European countries with particular emphasis on the nineteenth century". *Bulletin of the history of medicine* 29(3), 1955: 239-254.

72. AUBENQUE, L. "Les causes de décès en 1956". *Etudes statistiques,* supplément trimestriel du Bulletin mensuel de statistique, juil.-sept. 1957: 21-38.

73. BAUDETHIRI, T. *L'evoluzione demografica della Toscana del 1810 al 1889.* Torino, ILTE, 1960, XVI-138 p.

74. BELLETTINI, A. *La popolazione di Bologna dal secolo XV all'unificazione italiana.* Bologna, Zanichelli, 1961, 447 p.

75. BELTRAMI, D. *Storia della popolazione di Venezia dalla fine del secolo XVI alla caduta della Repubblica.* Padova, Cedam, 1954, 237 p. + appendice con 26 tav.

76. BREZNIK, D. "Neki kulturno-socijalni faktori smrtnosti dece u Jugoslaviji" (Certains facteurs sociaux culturels de la mortalité des enfants agés de 0 à 14 ans en Yougoslavie). *Socioloski pregled (Beograd)* 1, 1961: 91-111. (Résumé français.)

77. BRUNO, V. *Evoluzione della mortalita per cause di morte nella prima meta del secole XX in base alle tavole di mortalita del 1899-1902 e 1950-1953.* Pisa, Tornar, 1960, 124 p.

78. BURNS, C. M. *Infant and maternal mortality in relation to size of family and rapidity of breeding; a study in human responsibility.* Newcastle-upon-Tyne, University of Durham, King's college, Department of physiology, 1942, 247 p.

79. CHANDRASEKHAR, S. *Infant mortality in India, 1901-1955.* London, Allen and Unwin, 1959, 175 p.

80. CHIASSINO, G. "Sull'andamento della mortalita in Italia dal 1881 al 1951". *Rivista italiana di economia, demografia e statistica* 15(1-2), 1961: 53-72.

81. CONRAD, F. A. "Sex roles as factors in longevity". *Sociology and social research* 46(2), Jan. 1962: 195-202.

82. DALY, C.; HEADY, J. A.; MORRIS, J. N.; STEVENS, C. F. "The independent effects of social class, region, the mother's age and her parity on infant mortality". *Lancet* (1), 1955: 499-502.

83. D'ELIA, E. "Aspetti sociali della mortalita infantile in Sicilia". *Rivista italiana di economia, demografia e statistica* 5(1-2), 1951: 48-108.

84. DELLE PIANE, G.; DE CASTRO, D. "Le basi clinico-statistiche per un orientamento circa l'organizzazione dell'assistenza ostretica", pp. 57-71 in: *Atti della Societa italiana di ostetricia e ginecologia*, Napoli, 1956, vol. 65.

85. DOUGLAS, J. W. B. "Health and survival of infants in different social classes. A national survey". *Lancet* (2), 1951: 440-446.

86. DUBLIN, L. I. "The increasing mortality after age fortyfive: some causes and explanations". *Quarterly publications of the American statistical association* 15(117), March 1917: 511-523.

87. DURST, F. "Uzročna veza graviditeta i rane smrtnosti novorodjenceta" (The causes of foetal and neonatal death in pregnancy and labour). *Narodno zdravlje* 6(1-2), 1950: 10-23.

88. FEBVAY, M.; AUBENQUE, L. "La mortalité par catégorie socio-profession-

nelle". *Etudes statistiques*, supplément trimestriel du Bulletin mensuel de statistique, juil.-sept. 1957: 39-44.

89. FEBVAY, M.; CROZE, M. "Nouvelles données sur la mortalité infantile. Influence de la région et du milieu social". *Population* 9(3), juil.-sept. 54: 389-424.

90. FEDERICI, N. "L'evoluzione nel tempo della mortalita e di alcune sue particolari caratteristiche". *Genus* 6-8, 1943-1949: 385-395.

91. FEDERICI, N. "La mortalita differenziale dei due sessi e le sue possibil cause". *Statistica* 10(3), 1950: 274-320.

92. FEDERICI, N. "Osservazioni sull'evoluzione temporale di alcune caratteristiche della mortalita e sul problema della supermortalita maschile". *Bulletin de l'Institut international de statistique (Roma)* 32(3), 1954: 291-310.

93. FEDERICI, N. "Fattori sociali ed omogeneizzazione nel comportamento demografico". *Statistica* 15(4), 1955: 537-558.

94. FEDERICI, N. "L'andamento della mortalita giovanile nelle recenti tavole italiane", pp. 153-174 in: *Atti della XVIII riunione scientifica della Societa italiana di statistica*, Roma, 1958.

95. FEDERICI, N. "Caratteristiche territoriali della mortalita in Italia", pp. 9-89 in: *Atti della XX riunione scientifica della Societa italiana di statistica*, Roma, 1960.

96. FRANCE. STATISTIQUE GÉNÉRALE. *Table de mortalité des ouvriers mineurs, 1923-1928*. Paris, Imprimerie nationale, 1933, 39 p. (Présidence du Conseil, sous-secrétariat d'Etat de l'économie nationale, Statistique générale de la France).

97. GIANNELLI, G. "Della influenza della guerra sulla morbosita e mortalita". *Rivista italiana di economia, demografia e statistica* 1(2-3), 1947: 268-275.

98. GIBSON, J. R.; MCKEOWN, T. "Observations on all births (23,970) in Birmingham, 1947. 1: Duration of gestation". *British journal of social medicine* 4(4), Oct. 1950: 221-233.

99. GIBSON, J. R.; MCKEOWN, T. "Observations on all births (23,970) in Birmingham, 1947. 2: Birth weight". *British journal of social medicine* 5(2), April 51: 98-112.

100. GIBSON, J. R.; MCKEOWN, T. "Observations on all births (23,970) in Birmingham, 1947. 3: Survival". *British journal of social medicine* 5(3), July 1951: 177-183.

101. GIBSON, J. R.; MCKEOWN, T. "Observations on all births (23,970) in Birmingham, 1948. 5: Birth weight related to economic circumstances of parents". *British journal of social medicine* 5(4), Oct. 1951: 259-264.

102. GIBSON, J. R.; MCKEOWN, T. "Observations on all births (23,970) in Birmingham, 1947. 6: Birth weight, duration of gestation, and survival related to sex". *British journal of social medicine* 6(2), Apr. 52: 152-158.

103. GIBSON, J. R.; MCKEOWN, T. "Observations on all births (23,970) in Birmingham, 1947. 7: Effect of changing family size on infant mortality". *British journal of social medicine* 6(3), July 1952: 183-187.

104. GUERREIRO RAMOS, A. *Sociología de la mortalidad infantil*. México, Universidad Nacional, Instituto de investigaciones sociales, 1955, 253 p.

105. HADZIVUKOVIC, S. "Stope mortaliteta stanovnista Vojvodine po zanimanju u 1953 godini" (Les taux de mortalité de la population de Vojvodina selon la profession en 1953). *Privredna izgradnja* 3, 1958: 30-39.

106. HANSLUWKA, H. "Die Säuglingssterblichkeit in Österreich" (Infant mortality in Austria), pp. 402-413 in: *International Population Conference*, Vienne, 1959.

107. HEADY, J. A.; HEASMAN, M. A. *Social and biological factors in infant mortality*. London, H.M.S.O., 1958, 195 p. (General Register office. Special studies on medical and population subjects. 15.)

108. HENRY, L. "La mortalité infantile dans les familles nombreuses". *Population* 3(4), oct.-déc. 1948: 631-650.

109. HILL, A. B. *Internal migration and its effects upon the death-rates: with special reference to the county of Essex*. London, H.M.S.O., 1925, 124 p. (Medical research council. Special report series, 95.)

110. HUBER, M. "Mortalité suivant la profession, d'après les décès enregistrés en France pendant les années 1907 et 1908". *Bulletin de la Statistique générale de la France* 1(4), juil. 1912: 402-439, tabl.

111. HUMPHREYS, N. A. "Class mortality statistics". *Journal of the Royal statistical society* 50(2), June 1887: 255-285.

112. HUNT, E. P.; CHENOWETH, A. D. "Recent trends in infant mortality in the United States". *American journal of public health* 51(2), 1961: 190-207.

113. ILLSLEY, R. "Social class selection and class differences in relation to still births and infant deaths". *British medical journal* 4955, 1955: 1520-1524.

114. KARK, S. L.; CHESTER, J. "Survival in infancy". *South African journal of laboratory and clinical medicine* (2), 1956: 134-159.

115. KORAC, J. "Smrtnost i dohodak od poljoprivrede" (Deaths and income from agriculture). *Statistika revija* 6(1), 1956: 15-22. [Avec résumé anglais.]

116. KURCIEV, A.; KURCIEV, K. "Smrtnosta na doenčeta vo NR Makedonija" (Infant mortality in the People's Republic of Macedonia). *Godišnik na Ekonomskiot fakultet vo Skopje*, 1959: 85-131. [Avec résumé anglais.]

117. LENZI, R. "Sulla natimortalita". *Statistica* 14(1), 1954: 67-107.

118. LOGAN, W. P. D.; BENJAMIN, B. *Tuberculosis statistics for England and Wales, 1938 to 1955*. An analysis of trends and geographical distribution. London, H.M.S.O., 1957, 56 p. (General Register Office. Special studies on medical and population subjects. 10.)

119. MACURA, M. "Structure économique de la population et taux de natalité et

de mortalité". *Bulletin de l'Institut international de statistique* (*Rio de Janeiro*) 35(3), 1957: 475-484.

120. MADEK, S.; MITIC, F. "Pomor dojencadi u jugoslovenskim gradovima" (Infant mortality in Yugoslav towns in 1947). *Zbornik prvog kongresa lekara FNRJ* 2, 1949: 92-150 et 403-405, tabl.

121. MARKOVIĆ, S. "Morbiditet i mortalitet trudnih zena, porodilja i novorodjencadi u NR Srbiji 1950. god." (Morbidité et mortalité des femmes enceintes, des mères et nouveaux-nés dans la République Populaire de Serbie en 1950.)*Glasnik socijalne pedijatrije* 3(1-2), 1952: 55-74.

122. MARTIN, W. J. "A comparison of the trends of male and female mortality". *Journal of the Royal statistical society, Series A,* 114(3), 1951: 287-306.

123. MILLER, C. R.; SABAGH, G.; DINGMAN, H. F. "Latent class analysis and differential mortality". *Journal of the American statistical association* 57(298), June 1962: 430-438.

124. MILLER, F. J. W.; COURT, S. M.; WALTON, W. S.; KNOX, E. G. *Growing up in Newcastle upon Tyne.* London, Oxford University press, 1960, 369 p.

125. MORIYAMA, I. M.; GURALNICK, L. "Occupational and social class differences in mortality", pp. 61-73 in: *Trends and differentials in mortality.* 1955 annual conference of the Milbank memorial fund. New York, Milbank memorial fund, 1956, 168 p.

126. MORRIS, J. N.; HEADY, J. A. "Mortality in relation to the physical activity of work". *British journal of industrial medicine* 10, 1953: 245-257.

127. "Mortalité (La) infantile dans la région du Nord. Contribution aux travaux de l'Institut régional d'études et d'action démographiques du Nord de la France". *Etudes statistiques,* supplément trimestriel du Bulletin mensuel de statistique, janv.-mars 1956: 26-45, et juil.-sept. 1958: 19-38.

128. MORTARA, G. *Alcune caratteristiche demografiche differenziali del nord e del Sud dell'Italia.* Roma, Università degi studi, Istituto di demografia, 1960, 76 p. (Pubblicazioni dell'Istituto di demografia, 5.)

129. MORTARA, G. *Economia della popolazione.* Analisi delle relazioni tra fenomeni economici e fenomeni demografici. Torino, UTET, 1960, XVI-514 p.

130. NADDEO, A. *La mortalita in Italia dopo il 1950,* Roma, Universita degli studi, Istituto di demografia, 1959, 32 p. (Pubblicazioni dell'Istituto di demografia, 3.)

131. PATNO, M. E. "Mortality and economic level in an urban area". *Public health reports* 75(9), 1960: 841-851.

132. POPPER, L. "Frühinvalidität und Berufssterblichkeit" (Early incapacity and occupational mortality). *Statistischen Nachrichten* (*Wien*) 17(1), Jan. 1962; Supplement, 14 p.

133. RADCLIFFE, H. *Observations on the rate of mortality and sickness among members of friendly societies, particularised for various trades, occupations*

and localities. London, Manchester Unity of Independent Order of Old-fellows, 1850, 168 p.

134. SARVAN, M. "La mortalité péri-natale en Yougoslavie; notre expérience sur les causes biologiques, sociales et médicales". *Archives françaises de pédiatrie* 10(3), 1953: 263-267.

135. SCARDOVI, I. "Ricerche sperimentali intorno alle relazioni tra popolosita e movimento naturale della popolazione". *Statistica* 15(1), 1955: 187-224.

136. SCARDOVI, I. "Ricerche sulle manifestazioni demografiche differenziali dei comuni italiani". *Statistica* 18(2) et 18(3), 1958: 202-295 et 439-497.

137. SCARDOVI, I. "Aspetti della mortalita da infezione". *Rivista italiana di economia, demografia e statistica* 15(1-2), 1961: 73-104.

138. SCARDOVI, I. "In tema di 'supermortalita' maschile". *Statistica* 21(3), 1961: 551-613.

139. SCARDOVI, I. "Contributo allo studio delle componenti selettive della natimortalita". *Genus* 18, 1962: 144-181.

140. SCHWARTZ, P. "Les rapports entre la situation sociale et économique et la mortalité, par tuberculose et cancer" *La Presse médicale* 65(34), 1957: 821-823.

141. SOCIETY OF ACTUARIES. *Impairment study, 1951.* Chicago, Society of Actuaries, 1954, 156 p.

142. STEVENSON, T. H. C. "The social distribution of mortality from different causes in England and Wales, 1910-12". *Biometrika* 15, 1923: 382-400.

143. SUTTER, J.; TABAH, L. "La mortalité, phénomène biométrique". *Population* 7(1), janv.-mars 1952: 69-94.

144. TABAH, L. "La mortalité selon la classe sociale". *Le Concours médical* 77(28), 1955: 2839-2846.

145. TABAH, L. "La mortalité sociale: enquête nouvelle en Angleterre". *Population* 10(1), janv.-mars 1955: 57-78.

146. UNITED KINGDOM. AGRICULTURE, FISHERIES AND FOOD (MINISTRY). *Domestic food consumption and expenditure, 1957.* London, H.M.S.O., 1959, 137 p.

147. WOLFF, P. DE; MEERDINK, J. "La mortalité infantile à Amsterdam selon les groupes sociaux". *Population* 9(2), avr.-juin 1954: 293-314.

L. *Time Change and Generation Changes*

148. BEARD, R. E. "A theory of mortality based on actuarial, biological and medical considerations", pp. 611-626 in: *Proceedings of International Population Conference. New York, 1961.* Liège, International Union for scientific study of population, 1963, Vol. II.

149. DAVIDSON, A. R.; REID, A. R. "The calculation of rates of mortality. *Transactions of Faculty of actuaries in Scotland* 16, 1929: 183-232.

150. DAW, R. H. "Trend of mortality from tuberculosis". *Journal of the Institute of actuaries*, 76, 1950: 143-151.

151. DELAPORTE, P. J. "Changements de l'évolution de la mortalité en Europe pendant et après la seconde guerre mondiale/Changes in mortality trends in Europe during and after the Second World War", pp. 33-44 in: *Proceedings of the World Population Conference, Rome, 1954.* Papers vol. I.

152. DERRICK, V. P. A. "Observations on the changes in mortality indicated by the national record". *Journal of the Institute of actuaries* 58, 1927: 119-159.

153. MCKEOWN, T.; BROWN, R. G. "Medical evidence related to English population changes in the eighteenth century". *Population studies* 9(2), 1955: 119-141.

154. MCKEOWN, T.; RECORD, R. G. "Reasons for the decline of mortality in England and Wales during the nineteenth century". *Population studies* 16(2), 1962: 94-122.

155. SPICER, C. C. "The generation method of analysis applied to mortality from respiratory tuberculosis". *Journal of hygiene* 52(3), 1954: 361-368.

156. SPRINGETT, V. H. "A comparative study of tuberculosis mortality rates". *Journal of hygiene* 48(3), 1950: 361-395.

157. STOLNITZ, G. J. "A century of international mortality trends". *Population studies* 9(1), 1955: 24-55; 10(1), 1956: 17-42.

158. *Trends and differentials in mortality.* 1955 annual conference of the Milbank memorial fund. New York, Milbank memorial fund, 1956, 168 p.

Author index

Aitken-Swan, J., 31
Aleati, Giuseppe, 70
Anderson, Odin W., 71
Andrew, W., 17
Aubenque, L., 72, 88

Ballod, C., 23
Barber, R., 28
Baudethiri, T., 73
Beard, R. E., 148
Bellettini, Athos, 74
Beltrami, Daniele, 75
Benjamin, B., 1, 2, 118
Biraben, J. N., 65
Blaschko, M., 28
Bourgeois-[Pichat], Jean, 3, 4
Breznik, Dosan, 76
Brichler, M., 5
Brinton, H. P., 44
Brown, R. G., 153
Brownlee, John, 6
Bruno, Vincenzo, 77
Buckatzsch, E. J., 7, 8
Burns, C. M., 78

Case, R. A. M., 45, 46
Castillo Plaza, A., 24

Chalke, H. D., 29
Chandrasekhar, S., 79
Chenoweth, Alice D., 112
Chester, J., 114
Chiassino, Giuseppe, 80
Ciocco, A., 55
Clemmessen, J., 47
Comfort, A., 18
Conrad, Frederick A., 81
Court, S. M., 124
Cross, K. W., 60
Croze, Marcel, 89

Daly, C., 82
Davidson, A. R., 149
Daw, R. H., 150
Dawber, T. R., 9
De Castro, Diego, 84
Delaporte, Pierre J., 151
D'Elia, Eugenio, 83
Delle Piane, Giuseppe, 84
Derrick, V. P. A., 152
Dingman, H. F., 123
Doll, R., 61
Dorn, H. F., 10, 62
Douglas, J. W. B., 85
Dublin, L. I., 37, 86

Durst, Franjo, 87

Farr, W., 25
Febvay, Maurice, 88, 89
Federici, Nora, 90, 91, 92, 93, 94, 95
Frasier, E. S., 44

Giannelli, Giuseppe, 97
Gibson, J. R., 98, 99, 100, 101, 102, 103
Girard, Alain, 66, 67
Greenwood, Major, 11
Guerreiro Ramos, A., 104
Guralnick, L., 125

Hadzivukovic, Stevan, 105
Hammond, E. C., 63
Hansluwka, H., 106
Hauser, P. M., 48
Heady, J. A., 82, 107, 126
Heasman, M. A., 107
Henry, L., 67
Henry, Louis, 108
Hewitt, D., 30
Hill, A. B., 61, 109
Horn, 63
Hosker, M. E., 45, 46
Huber, M., 110
Humphreys, Noel A., 111
Hunt, Eleanor, P., 112

Illsley, R., 113

Kark, S. L., 114
Kellgren, J. H., 31
Kitagawa, E. M., 48
Knox, E. G., 124
Korac, Josip, 115

Koven, A. L., 44
Kraus, A. S., 56
Kurciev, Aleksandar, 116
Kurciev, Kiril, 116

Lawrence, J. S., 31
Ledermann, Sully, 49
Lenzi, Romolo, 117
Lilienfield, A. M., 56
Logan, W. P. D., 118

McDonald, D. B., 46
McDowell, L. A., 60
McFie, J., 38
McKeown, Thomas, 98, 99, 100, 101, 102, 103, 153, 154
Macura, Milos, 119
Madek, Slavko, 120
Markovic, Smilja, 121
Marks, H. H., 37
Martin, W. J., 122
Masselink, R. J., 19
Meerdink, J., 147
Merritt, H. H., 19
Miller, C. R., 123
Miller, F. J. W., 124
Miller, W. B., 68
Mitic, Fedor, 120
Moore, J. E., 19
Moriyama, I. M., 125
Morris, J. N., 82, 126
Mortara, Giorgio, 128, 129
Moser, C. A., 12, 13
Murray, M., Bruce, 39

Naddeo, Alighiero, 130
Newsholme, Arthur, 26
Nistri, R., 67

Patno, M. E., 131
Paul, Benjamin D., 68
Pauling, L., 40
Pearson, J. T., 46
Pearson, Karl, 14
Perry, K. M. A., 50
Popper, Ludwig, 132
Posner, E., 60

Radcliffe, Henry, 133
Record, R. G., 154
Reid, A. R., 149
Rockstein, M., 41
Russell, W. T., 35

Sabach, G., 123
Sarvan, M., 134
Scardovi, Italo, 135, 136, 137, 138, 139
Schwartz, P., 140
Scott, J. A., 32
Scott, W., 13
Sheps, Mindel C., 58

Shock, N. W., 20
Smith, C. M., 33
Spicer, C. C., 155
Springett, V. H., 156
Stein, L., 34
Stevens, C. F., 82
Stevenson, T. H. C., 142
Stewart, A., 30
Stewart, A. M., 35
Stocks, P., 27, 36
Stockwell, E. G., 54
Stolnitz, G. J., 157
Sukhatme, P. V., 42
Sutter, Jean, 143

Tabah, Léon, 143, 144, 145
Tocher, J. F., 14

Upchurch, Harley M., 69

Walton, W. S., 124
Widdowson, E. M., 43
Wolff, P., 147